T... ...aph Series

E...

Number 3

ite

THE TEXTILE INSTITUTE
10 Blackfriars Street, Manchester M3 5DR
© The Textile Institute 1975
First Published 1975
ISBN 0 900739 21 5

Printed by Richard Bates Ltd., Wythenshawe, Manchester

CONTENTS

PART II: THE TREATMENT AND DISPOSAL OF EFFLUENTS

WATER SUPPLIES AND THE TREATMENT AND DISPOSAL OF EFFLUENTS

By A. H. Little, B.Sc., F.R.I.C., F.T.I., M.Inst.W.P.C.

PART I: WATER SUPPLIES

1. WATER REQUIREMENTS FOR THE TEXTILE INDUSTRY

1.1 Introduction

The water requirements for the textile industry vary with the use to which the water is to be put, and in some cases the processes within a works will demand different water qualities. In addition, water for steam-raising is usually needed in mills, and this again may require different properties in the water supply. The supply requirements therefore differ with individual firms, and each tends to solve the problem according to the available supplies and facilities. Some firms have a large supply of good water that meets their process needs, usually after a pre-treatment such as sedimentation in a mill lodge, with some additional treatment for the boiler water. Others may have several sources of supply—river, bore-hole, and town's main—and use these where they are most suitable. The question as to which is most suitable may not always be answered correctly. There is a tendency to regard mains water as pure and to keep this for special purposes while using one of the other supplies for, say, bulk-washing on the assumption that it is less pure; this may not always be true. Town water, although potable, is often unsuitable for textile processes such as package-dyeing because it contains suspended matter and soluble calcium and magnesium salts; filtration and softening may be necessary before it can be employed with confidence in a process in which impurities can filter out upon yarn or fabric.

Analysis of a water supply gives much useful information and is essential when a new supply is being considered for textile processing. This has been realized for a long time, and it is on record[1] that John Dalton analysed the water supply for the firm of Sykes & Co. at Stockport and declared it suitable for the purpose.

The analytical results may not tell the whole story because they depend upon samples taken at particular times, whereas supplies, particularly surface water but also bore-hole water, vary considerably throughout the year. Knowledge of the extent of this variation is required, especially on what are likely to be the worst conditions, and if possible sampling should be done in the winter and spring in the British Isles, when the run-off after rain tends to be heavy, as well as in the summer, when the river levels are low. At low river flows, the effects of pollution are greater than they are at high flows, and, if there is any contamination that is likely to affect textile processing, this will show up more in samples taken at such times. Bore-hole water is usually more uniform than surface water, particularly when there is no intrusion from different strata. However, change may occur with the seasons because of fluctuations in the ground water. This can sometimes be seen when iron or manganese contamination occurs during a limited part of the year.

1.2 Process-water Usage

The quantity of water needed for textile processing depends greatly upon the work being done. Some processes involving simple treatment of yarn or fabric with an aqueous solution, such as yarn-sizing or back-filling, require very little water, whereas others, composed of a sequence of operations with many rinses, demand large quantities. There was, until recently, little direct information on the requirements of the textile industry. However, several of the textile research associations (Shirley Institute, Wira, and Hatra) have made surveys of water usage in the trade, and a fairly comprehensive picture is emerging of the processes that use substantial amounts[2-4].

Many factors affect the usage, and not all of them are under the control of the textile works. As the processes become more complex, the water usage increases, particularly when each treatment is followed by one or more washes, and, because of this, works carrying out a variety of treatments in sequence, such as those involved in printing, use more water than a dye works that scours and dyes fabrics by simple processes. The results obtained in the surveys should allow forecasting of the usage for a works in which the processes and the type of fabric treated are known.

The demand for water in a works fluctuates through the day, and storage capacity has to be adequate to meet peak loads. Service reservoirs or tanks are usually available, but the method of distribution should be such as to give ample supplies in, say, the late morning or afternoon, when much washing-off is done.

Examples of the specific usage of water (that is, the volume of water per unit weight of textile material) for various processes are given in Table I.

Table I

Water Usage in Textile Processing

Material	Process	Water Usage			
		(gal/lb)		(l./kg)	
		Average	Range	Average	Range
Cotton	Desizing—continuous	4.5	2.0–9.2	45	20–92
Cotton	Scouring—continuous	3.0	0.3–9.4	30	3–94
Cotton	Scouring—jig	1.8	0.1–4.8	18	1–48
Cotton	Bleaching, hypochlorite—continuous	0.7	0.4–1.3	7	4–13
Cotton	Bleaching, hypochlorite—batch	6.9	2.1–17.3	69	21–173
Cotton	Bleaching, peroxide—continuous	3.8	1.3–6.4	38	13–64
Cotton	Bleaching, peroxide—kier	3.7	0.8–8.0	37	8–30
Cotton	Bleaching, chlorite—continuous	1.0	1.0–1.3	10	10–13
Cotton and man-made fibres	Dyeing—continuous	3.8	0.9–6.3	38	9–63
Cotton and man-made fibres	Dyeing—jig	7.7	0.4–29.7	77	4–298
Cotton and man-made fibres	Dyeing—winch	18.3	2.8–54.0	183	28–541
Cotton and man-made fibres	Dyeing—beam	9.2	3.1–16.6	92	31–166
Wool: loose	Washing	1.3	0.3–2.6	13	3–26
Wool: loose	Dyeing	5.2	2.6–13.1	52	26–131
Wool: top	Washing	0.4	0.02–0.9	4	0.2–9
Wool: top	Dyeing	3.8	2.0–7.0	38	20–70
Wool yarn: hanks	Scouring	1.3	0.3–4.1	13	3–41
Wool yarn: hanks	Dyeing	5.4	2.5–11.1	54	25–111
Wool yarn: package	Dyeing	4.7	1.0–11.2	47	10–112
Woollen piece	Scouring (dolly machine)	9.4	3.9–17.4	94	39–174
Woollen piece	Milling in soap	6.2	3.5–9.9	62	35–99
Woollen piece	Dyeing	12.3	2.6–38.6	123	26–387
Worsted piece	Scouring	13.4	4.7–49.4	134	47–495
Worsted piece	Milling in soap	7.0	3.4–17.2	70	34–172
Worsted piece	Dyeing	15.1	8.6–19.8	151	86–198
Nylon hose		12.0	5.8–34.3	120	58–344
Nylon socks		12.8	5.8–27.0	128	58–271
Acrylic-fibre garments		15.7	7.1–61.0	157	71–611
Wool garments		35.3	18.6–86.3	354	186–865
Wool hanks		5.6	1.9–10.7	56	19–107

1.3 Water for Textile Processing

This has to meet fairly stringent demands, and the main criteria are:

(i) freedom from suspended solids and from substances that can give staining in processing;

(ii) no great excess of acid or alkali, i.e., a pH range of $\pm$ 2 on either side of the neutral point;

(iii) freedom from substances affecting the textile processes, such as iron, manganese, calcium or magnesium salts, and heavy metals;

(iv) non-corrosiveness to tanks and pipe lines; and

(v) freedom from substances that give rise to foaming or unpleasant odours.

The effects of deviation from these requirements are discussed below.

(i) The main requirement of water for textiles is freedom from solid particles in suspension or from substances that could give rise to solids in processing. Solid particles may be filtered out by yarn packages and by fabrics, and, if the deposit is dark, stains occur or the stains can absorb colour and become dark. For example, staining results from the deposition of dark peaty solids from moorland waters and also from calcium and magnesium soaps derived from hard waters. The hydroxides and soaps of other metals, such as iron, manganese, and aluminium, give stains caused either by their colour or by binding coloured solids. The well-known kier stains on cotton are coloured by dark humus particles or by iron and manganese hydroxides and are firmly bound by insoluble metal soaps, including those of iron, calcium, and magnesium. Such stains are very difficult to remove owing to their insolubility and resistance to wetting.

To avoid such troubles, the water supply has to be freed from solid particles and needs to have a very low content of iron, manganese, aluminium, calcium, and magnesium.

Once waters are freed from solids and are soft, it is important to prevent further contamination, particularly by iron rust from piping. Distribution and storage should be in materials that cannot contaminate the water, such as asbestos–cement, plastics, or lined pipes and containers. Occasional complaints come from the presence of lead in water, usually through dark lead sulphide staining, but these generally arise from contact with lead or solder on the plant and rarely from contamination of the water, although this could occur when very soft water is in contact with new lead piping.

(ii) Excess acid or alkali can interfere with some textile processes and may also indicate a deviation from normal in the water-purification process.

Natural waters may contain alkalinity owing to the presence of bicarbonates, usually those of calcium, magnesium, sodium, and potassium. Some soft waters from sources containing peat may be slightly acidic, whereas streams receiving water from mine drainage may be strongly acid. Purification treatments usually result in a change in pH of the water. Softening by zeolite or resin processes leaves the water containing considerable amounts of sodium bicarbonate, with a pH near to 8, whereas the lime–soda-softening process may give higher alkalinities, the water containing sodium carbonate and sometimes hydroxide, with a pH between 10 and 12.

(iii) Substances that could affect processing are metals such as copper and iron, which can act as activators in bleaching operations. Almost always, these have a deleterious effect on the textile material, and they should be excluded. Copper is not usually a natural component of water and is picked up by contact with copper and brass fittings or pipes. Particularly bad contamination with copper can arise from the use of ammonia solutions in vessels exposed to the air. Copper vessels and brass fittings are rapidly attacked under these conditions. Care has to be taken to avoid copper-containing fittings on bleaching plant and, if the source of the copper cannot be traced, to employ a sequestering agent to prevent its activity from affecting the process. Iron is normally removed by one of the methods described in Section 4.

Hard water will, of course, affect soaping processes and consume soap by the formation of insoluble calcium and magnesium soaps. In each 1000 gal (4546 l.) of water, for every degree of hardness (17 p.p.m.), over 1 lb (0·454 kg) of soap is put out of action. This is fairly well known, but it is not commonly realized that synthetic detergents are affected deleteriously by the hardness of the water, although not to the same extent as soaps. This can be counteracted to some extent by the addition of materials such as polyphosphates, which sequester the calcium and magnesium ions, but this is an expensive way of softening water.

In water for enzyme-desizing and for peroxide-bleaching, some hardness can be tolerated, because in water of medium hardness the bath stability is better than it is in very soft water. However, too high a concentration of calcium or magnesium makes a peroxide bleach bath too stable. To avoid the necessity for the provision of a special supply of unsoftened water, an addition of magnesium sulphate can be made to the soft supply, and this gives the desired stability. Hard water can affect vat-dyeing operations detrimentally, and a soft-water supply is required.

The alkalinity of water arising from softening is generally harmless, but in some processes it can cause trouble. Thus, in the dyeing of rayon with certain direct colours in closed machines, the alkalinity can dissolve sufficient reducing substances to cause reduction of some of the dye, with destruction of the colour. This can be avoided by the addition of ammonium sulphate[5]. In dyeing nylon and Acrilan, the pH of the water should be uniform because some of the dyes employed are pH-sensitive[6].

(iv) Corrosion of tanks and pipelines can take place with soft water, particularly if the pH is low. Natural water containing free carbon dioxide, but no alkali or dissolved oxygen, attacks iron pipes, ferrous bicarbonate passing into solution. This is partly avoided if the water is aerated, but even with oxygen present there is a certain amount of iron corrosion. Raising the pH by the addition of alkali as lime, calcium carbonate, or sodium silicate will prevent this type of corrosion. A type of corrosion frequently encountered is the attack of iron in condensate return lines from dyeing machines. Low pH from the presence of carbon dioxide and oxygen dissolved in the water gives rapid attack of iron, steel, and galvanized piping under the hot conditions. This occurs almost entirely in the region where liquid water is in contact with the metal.

(v) Foaming and unpleasant odours from water depend upon the source. Surface water, particularly in rivers, often contains detergents and detergent residues from town drainage. With the soft detergents now in use, this trouble is not so bad as it was a few years ago, but appreciable quantities still get into some rivers, even though the bulk is removed in sewage-purification treatment. In the same way, unpleasant odours can come from chemical residues that escape the purification process. The removal of persistent residues that give rise to foaming or smells could be an expensive process because they may be from materials that have not been amenable to treatment. If the normal purification treatments by flocculation and filtration or sedimentation are not effective, it may be necessary to employ absorption methods using active carbon or chlorination. Unpleasant odours sometimes come from the decomposition of vegetable matter and algae in reservoirs, and in this case the remedy lies in cleaning of the storage system.

1.4   Canteens and Toilets

Firms often provide canteen facilities for their staff and are obliged to provide toilets. The water requirements can be estimated from the numbers of persons involved, the usual amounts being 10 gal (45 l.) per head per day for those using the canteens and 20 gal (90 l.) per head per day for toilets. Since it is necessary for potable water to be provided for food preparation and drinking-water supplies, it is customary to employ mains water, but, for isolated works without piped water, care has to be exercised in the choice of supply. Water from deep wells may be sufficiently pure for employment in these circumstances, but before use the water should be examined by a qualified person to make certain that it is uncontaminated. Water from other sources, such as streams or shallow wells, should be regarded with suspicion unless it is proved by tests to be free from organic and bacterial contamination. Where a potable-water source is in use, great care must be exercised to ensure that no cross-connexion can be made with any other supply.

1.5   Fire-fighting Supplies

Local conditions will control the need for the provision of water supplies for fire-fighting. In towns, there are generally hydrants on the water mains or a pressure supply for sprinkler devices. In country districts with no mains supply, a pressurized service may be provided by the installation of a large tank elevated above the buildings of the mill. With this available, the main concerns are to ensure that the tank is large enough and that sufficient head is maintained in the supply line to keep the tank full. Sometimes, under peak-loading conditions, the pressure in the line is insufficient to replenish the tank, and, if pumps are shut down at the end of the day, the tank may be left only partly full. The conditions to be met for the provision of water for fighting fires are best discussed with the local Fire Brigade Superintendent, who will give details of the supply required and of any additional facilities, such as providing access to mill lodges for suction hoses of pumps, and any special precautions that are necessary.

2.   PROPERTIES OF WATER

2.1   Introduction

Water is so often taken for granted that few people consider what is needed in a supply until the matter is forced upon them by a shortage or a change in properties that affect the running of a works. In this section, many of the properties are listed, with notes on what is desirable in water for textile uses. The more stringent requirements may not be needed for all processes, but, where only one supply is available, this has to meet the strictest limits[7] (see Table II).

Table II

Quality or Substance	Acceptable Limits (mg/1.)
Turbidity	Less than 5
Suspended solids	Less than 5
Colour	Less than 10 units (Hazen)
pH	7–9
Acidity/alkalinity	Less than 100 as $CaCO_3$
Hardness	Less than 70 as $CaCO_3$
Iron	Less than 0·3*
Manganese	Less than 0·05
Copper	Less than 0·01
Lead or heavy metals	Less than 0·01
Aluminium	Less than 0·25
Silica	Less than 10
Sulphate	Less than 250
Sulphide	Less than 1
Chloride	Less than 250
Phosphate	No limit
Dissolved oxygen	No limit
Carbon dioxide	Less than 50
Nitrite	Less than 0·5
Chlorine	Less than 0·1
Ammonia	Less than 0·5
Oil, grease, fat, soap	Less than 1
Fluorescent brightening agents	Less than 0·2
Total solids	Less than 500

* A lower limit, 0·1 mg/1., for some uses.

2.2   Contaminants and Their Limits

2.2.1   *Colour*

This is usually taken as indicative of contamination as either suspended or soluble matter. Limits of not more than 5 units (Hazen) have been quoted, but this means little unless it is known that the colour is not due to suspended matter.

The methods of purification by flocculation and filtration that are employed will usually bring the colour down to a low level.

2.2.2   *Turbidity*

Turbidity is often associated with colour but is really indicative of solid matter in suspension as distinct from soluble substances in solution. The solid matter may contribute to the colour if it is itself coloured.

The opacity of water may arise from a variety of materials in suspension, and samples from different sources may be equally opaque but contain widely varying weights of solid matter. For textile uses, the quantity of solid matter in suspension must be very low, particularly if the solids are dark in colour, and, since the detrimental effects are staining due to the deposition and filtration of solid matter, the requirements of water in this respect are dealt with below under 'suspended solids'. The colour and turbidity of the supply are, however, useful indications of the presence of unwanted solid matter and a warning of the need for treatment before use.

Turbidity is generally associated with surface-water supplies, and ground water, particularly that from deep wells or bore-holes, is usually quite clear. In certain cases, there may be deposition of solid matter from ground water on standing, such as occurs in supplies containing iron or manganese, where, on exposure to the atmosphere, the water picks up oxygen or loses carbon dioxide, which results in precipitation of insoluble hydroxides. The stability of the water has therefore to be taken into account in assessing the value of a water supply and the need for treatment before use.

2.2.3 *Suspended Solids*

Supplies of water for the wet processing of textiles must be very low in suspended solids and not liable to deposit matter on standing. For general use, a limit of 5 mg/l. is desirable, but for some purposes, such as package-bleaching and package-dyeing, an even lower limit is required. For these kinds of use, the water must be substantially free from solid matter because the packages form very efficient filters, and any deposition of solids is shown as dark stains on the package surfaces. For the treatment of such water, it is not uncommon for it to be subjected to flocculation with alum or alum-sodium aluminate, followed by pressure filtration, or for a filter aid to be added and the water then passed through a filter with fine clearances, such as a meta-filter. In addition, water that has been softened and clarified should be carried only in pipes that will not corrode and add corrosion products to the system. Iron pipes, even though galvanized when new, may show internal corrosion, and this can produce rust as suspended matter.

2.2.4 *Hardness*

For some, but not all, textile processes, it is desirable to remove the hardness of the water for process work. In any operations that include the use of soap, the hardness is detrimental, because lime soaps are formed that waste soap and give rise to sticky deposits on fabric and machines.

On the other hand, there are some operations, such as peroxide-bleaching and the rinsing of acid from fabric, which may be more effective in hard water. There is therefore a case to be made for softening of some, if not all, the process water. This softening is usually done by means of the base-exchange process or some variation of this, giving water of near-zero hardness. If just a few processes need soft water, it is practicable to pipe the soft water to the machines concerned, but, where the requirements are scattered, it is usually more convenient to soften most of the supply.

2.2.5 *Metals*

The metal content of water should be low (in iron, manganese, copper, aluminium, and heavy metals), for this can cause staining or interference with processes. Methods are given in Section 4.3 for the removal of those metals that can be troublesome.

Limits for textile processing are indicated in Table II.

2.2.6 *Silica*

Small amounts are found in natural waters, but the only likely major source is soluble silicate used in water treatment. Its presence in appreciable amounts is indicative of incorrect dosing, which should be rectified, but small amounts are unlikely to be troublesome in processing unless hard water is in use. With hard water, deposits of calcium and magnesium silicate are formed.

2.2.7 *Sulphate*

This may be present in natural sources such as mine water but may also come from atmospheric pollution, from flocculation with alum, and from reuse of water. In moderate amounts, it is not troublesome, but for dyeing work it may be desirable to keep the concentration reasonably constant so as not to affect the rate of dyeing.

2.2.8 *Sulphite and Sulphide*

These may cause difficulties with processes, and sulphide may cause staining, so a low level in water is requisite; both can be removed by acidification and aeration or by oxidation with chlorine.

2.2.9 *Chloride*

Some chloride may come from natural sources, with occasionally large amounts from salt-bearing rock strata, but its presence is usually taken as indicating sewage contamination of the supply. Some rivers may contain 200–300 mg/1. normally, with peak figures of several times this level. Again, as for sulphate, the main requirement is to keep the level fairly constant in process water so as not to affect dyeing.

2.2.10 *Chlorine*

Free chlorine in small amount (0·1–0·2 p.p.m.), such as might come from water sterilization, is not likely to be troublesome, but, if in excess of this, it could be objectionable. Removal can be effected by the addition of sodium bisulphite, but the source of the chlorine should be located and stopped, so that the trouble does not persist.

2.2.11 *Phosphate*

This is found in natural waters in small quantities (3 p.p.m. or less) and at this level is unlikely to cause any process trouble. The amounts in rivers are tending to increase because of discharges of sewage effluents containing phosphates derived from domestic detergents. Additions of sodium hexametaphosphate are useful in preventing precipitation of calcium carbonate, which sometimes follows the use of lime–soda-softening.

2.2.12 *Nitrite and Nitrate*

These may be found in surface waters containing nitrogenous matter from sewage. Small amounts are unlikely to cause difficulty, but large amounts can cause troubles in dyeing and can lead to staining with amino compounds.

2.2.13 *Carbon Dioxide*

Carbon dioxide is found free in some natural waters and is formed in hard waters by acidification. Although innocuous in processing, it can cause corrosion of iron piping. It is easily removed by aeration.

2.2.14 *Dissolved Oxygen*

Most waters contain some dissolved oxygen, and, when in equilibrium with the atmosphere, the amounts will depend upon the water temperature. The lack of oxygen may cause occasional trouble with easily reduced substances and possibly give conditions where anaerobic corrosion could occur. Ordinary rusting is usually ascribed to oxidation of ferrous ions in solutions by dissolved oxygen, and its presence is therefore a factor in corrosion although not one that is controllable.

2.2.15 *Oxygen Demand*

The consumption of oxygen or oxidizing agents by water arising from the presence of reducing substances, usually organic, is of value in the assessment of trade effluents and sewage but is not of great importance for process waters. In cases of contamination of water, it may be of value for indicating the extent and sources of pollution.

2.2.16   *Ammonia*

The presence of free ammonia or of protein material is almost always an indication of contamination of the water with sewage or trade effluents, such as gas liquor.

2.2.17   *Greasy Contaminants*

Oil, grease, fat, and soap arising from pollution may be troublesome through the coating of channels, pipes, and filter beds. It is essential to remove them from water to prevent the soiling of fabric.

2.2.18   *Total Solids*

The soluble salts in water vary with the composition, and, provided that they are not excessive in quantity and are reasonably constant in amount, they do not constitute a hazard. Measurements of conductivity will show how the ionized soluble matter varies.

2.2.19   *Fluorescent Brightening Agents*

The presence of these in water, even in small amounts, can cause difficulties in dyeing pastel shades if they are substantive to the fibres being processed. It has been found that as little as 0·5 mg/l. will produce appreciable shade differences. The simplest way to test for their presence is to evaporate a known volume of water to small bulk and dye a swatch of cotton and synthetic-fibre material. Examination under ultra-violet radiation will show the presence of any brightening agent.

2.2.20   *Surface-active Agents*

These are being found more and more in water supplies but are unlikely to cause process difficulties unless anionic material combines with cation-active agents being used in finishing. Their presence is, however, indicative of pollution, and any sudden increase in foaming in the raw water should be regarded with suspicion.

2.3   Sampling and Analysis

2.3.1   *Introduction*

A sample of water must represent in all aspects the main bulk from which it was taken. If the main bulk is variable, as may be the case with surface water or shallow bore-holes, the sampling procedure must take this into account, and with mains water the collection of specimens must be preceded by thorough flushing of the main and distribution pipes to get rid of any water that has been standing. Water lying in pipes can change in character and pick up metals such as copper or lead, so that it is not representative of the bulk supply. Many complaints of lead contamination have arisen from failure to observe this precaution.

For variable supplies, several samples must be taken, preferably automatically, so that the extent of any variation can be estimated. An unwanted component can sometimes be present at long intervals, and this can be very troublesome. For example, metal contamination is sometimes found in bore-hole water only at certain times in the year, possibly because of changes in the ground-water level, and normal sampling may show negative results for most of the remainder of the time.

Collection of samples must be in perfectly clean glass or plastics bottles, used only for water analysis, and precautions taken to prevent contamination in handling. An excellent account of water-sampling and analysis is given by Holden[7].

Analytical methods for water analysis are generally well established, and, for most of the tests, information is available in textbooks[7], in the 'Approved Methods' of the Institution of Water Engineers[8], or in the 'Analysis of Raw, Potable, and Waste Waters'[9]. Brief details of the appropriate methods are given below, although for working details reference should be made to the collected methods or to the original papers.

2.3.2 *Turbidity*

This is bound up with the content of suspended solids and can be estimated by matching samples against known standards of dispersed solids[7] or more readily by direct measurement in an instrument such as the EEL Hazometer. However, the interest is usually in the filterable or settlable solids, and these are normally determined by the methods given in the next test.

2.3.3 *Suspended Solids*

These are dealt with below, in Section 13 of Part II.

2.3.4 *Colour*

In natural waters, colour is often difficult to dissociate from turbidity, and any measurements must be made on samples that are substantially free from suspended matter. Comparisons are usually made visually with platinum-cobalt standards prepared from mixtures of chloroplatinic acid and cobalt chloride. In the Hazen[7,10] scale, 1 unit = 1 mg/l.

2.3.5   *pH and Acidity/Alkalinity*

The pH of water does not necessarily denote the same concept as the acidity or alkalinity, although they are related[8]. The pH is the logarithmic expression of the reciprocal of the hydrogen-ion concentration, whereas the others are measures of the quantity of alkali or acid present in the sample, determined quantitatively between appropriate pH limits. In dilute solutions of strong bases or acids, the quantities are comparable, but for weak bases or acids they are not. The same pH may be given by a very small quantity of a strong acid or by a much larger quantity of a weak acid or a mixture of such an acid with its salts. This makes it important to select the right measure for the purpose in view. The pH is normally determined by direct potentiometric measurement by means of a glass electrode, which can be employed without alteration to the character of the specimen and can be used in turbid or coloured water. Rough estimations of pH can be made quickly with indicators, either in liquid form or as test papers.

Alkalinity is determined by titration with dilute (0·02N) hydrochloric or sulphuric acid, a pH meter or indicator being used to show the end-point near pH 4·5. For alkaline waste water, higher concentrations can be determined by using appropriately stronger acid for titration.

Acidity is measured in a similar way by using dilute sodium hydroxide as the titrant.

2.3.6   *Hardness*

The hardness of water depends principally upon the concentration of calcium and magnesium[7]. It has often been divided into temporary hardness due to the presence of bicarbonates, which are decomposed by boiling, and permanent hardness due to the presence of sulphates, chlorides, and nitrates, which are unaffected by boiling. For some time, the estimation was by titration with soap, giving insoluble calcium and magnesium soaps, but this is now replaced by the EDTA titration[7]. This method arises from the formation of complexes of calcium and magnesium ions with EDTA (ethylenediamine tetra-acetic acid). The sample is titrated at a pH near 10 with EDTA solution until a colour change occurs at the end-point with Eriochrome Black T or some other similar indicator. A procedure for waters of low hardness, i.e., less than 10 mg/l., is given in B.S.2690: Part 4: 1967[11]. By modification of the conditions of test and the use of an appropriate indicator, it is possible to determine separately the calcium content of a sample. The difference between this and the total hardness then gives the magnesium content.

2.3.7 *Iron*

In surface water, the content of soluble iron is usually low, and most of that present is in the form of insoluble hydroxides or combined with organic matter. If the water is from bore-holes and contains no oxygen, soluble iron may be present as ferrous bicarbonate. However, on exposure to air, this is oxidized and precipitated as ferric hydroxide, which is usually removed from the water before use.

Iron is determined colorimetrically, usually with thiocyanate, which gives a red colour in acid solution[8]. The sensitivity can be improved and interference from other ions diminished by extracting the red colour with a solvent.

Other methods of test use thioglycollic acid (producing a pink colour) and *o*-phenanthroline[7].

2.3.8 *Manganese*

This metal is usually found in water associated with iron, and the soluble bicarbonate is oxidized and precipitated as hydroxide in the same way as for iron, although a higher pH is needed for complete precipitation. Test methods usually convert the manganese to permanganate, which is estimated by its pink colour, by comparison with standards, or absorptiometrically[9]. Oxidation to the higher state is usually performed with persulphate or periodate.

A qualitative test for manganese uses 'tetramethyl base' (4,4'-tetra-methyldiaminodiphenylmethane)[7], which gives a blue colour at low concentrations.

2.3.9 *Aluminium*

Treatment with acid before analysis is necessary to get all the aluminium into solution in an ionized form. Several colorimetric methods of test are available. Haematoxylin[8] gives a bright blue colour and is suitable for visual comparisons, but the colour of the reagent prevents spectrophotometry. Interference by iron or copper is prevented by the addition of cyanide. Aluminon (ammonium aurine tricarboxylate) can be used for absorptiometric work and is reliable, interference from iron being minimized by the addition of thioglycollic acid. A method using Solochrome Cyanine R[12] is stated to have shown promise for the control of aluminium residues in the treatment of water with alum.

2.3.10   *Lead*

Samples must be collected after thorough flushing of pipes, and testing must be done soon after collection. A colorimetric test employing dithizone is generally employed. The test is sensitive, and, in view of the low concentrations of lead encountered, it is necessary to run control tests on all reagents[13]. Reasonably good sensitivity can also be obtained with sulphide, and the method is simple[8].

2.3.11   *Copper*

The colorimetric test in which sodium diethyldithio-carbamate is used is extensively employed and gives satisfactory results when tartaric acid is added to remove interference from iron, calcium, and magnesium[8]. The yellow–brown colour can be extracted with a solvent, which improves the sensitivity of the test.

Other reagents that have been employed are Cuproine[14] (2,2'-diquinolyl), Cuprethol[10] (2-hydroxyethyldithiocarbamate), and Bathocuproine (2,9-dimethyl-4,7-diphenyl-1,10-phenanthroline and biscyclohexanoneoxalyl-dihydrazone)[14].

2.3.12   *Zinc*

Several sensitive colorimetric methods are available, such as those using ferrocyanide[8], dithizone and 'Zincon'[10,14] (2-carboxy-2-hydroxy-5-sulphoformazobenzene). Various methods are employed to prevent interference from iron, copper, and other metals.

2.3.13   *Chromium*

The metal is usually estimated colorimetrially with diphenylcarbazide[8,10], giving a violet colour, when the chromium is hexavalent. Removal of organic matter and oxidation are necessary in the determination of the total chromium in a sample.

2.3.14   *Silica*

Silica may be derived from natural sources or may come from water-treatment chemicals or detergent mixtures. Estimation is by the formation of the molybdate complex, either as the yellow acid or as its blue reduction product[8].

2.3.15 *Sulphate*

The most convenient method is by the addition of excess barium chloride and back titration with EDTA, as in the determination of hardness[15]. For high concentrations, the classical gravimetric method of precipitation and weighing as barium sulphate is suitable; silica can interfere[8].

2.3.16 *Sulphide*

The iodometric method is suitable for moderate concentrations by using excess iodine and back-titrating with thiosulphate[9],[16]. Interference can be avoided by the precipitation of zinc sulphide and filtration. The zinc sulphide is then transferred to a vessel through which passes an inert gas, such as nitrogen or carbon dioxide. Acid is added and the hydrogen sulphide absorbed in zinc acetate. The zinc sulphide produced is then treated with iodine, and the quantity of iodine reduced is determined by titration with thiosulphate.

2.3.17 *Chloride*

Analysis by the old-established technique of direct titration with silver nitrate (Mohr's method)[9] or back titration (Volhard's method)[8] is both suitable and adequate.

A newer method is titration with mercuric nitrate in acid solution, diphenylcarbazone being used as indicator. This is apparently less affected by phosphate than Mohr's method[10].

2.3.18 *Phosphate*

Phosphate can be estimated to give the phosphomolybdate as ortho-phosphate by using the colour developed with ammonium molybdate. This gives a blue colour after reduction. The molybdenum blue can be estimated in a spectrophotometer. Where meta-phosphate, pyro-phosphate, or poly-phosphate may be present, as in waters containing residues of bleach liquors or detergent mixtures, the solution should be boiled with acid to hydrolyse these before the determination is made[7].

2.3.19 *Nitrogen: Ammoniacal*

The method for the determination of free or combined ammoniacal nitrogen is given below in Section 13.2.8 of Part II.

2.3.20 *Nitrogen: Organic*

Oxidized nitrogen is reduced to ammonia with Devarda's alloy, and this, together with any free ammoniacal nitrogen, is removed from the sample by boiling the alkaline solution. The residue is treated with sulphuric acid and boiled. After dilution, the determination of ammonia is carried out in the normal way[9].

2.3.21 *Nitrogen: Nitrate*

Several methods are available, those most frequently used employing reduction of the nitrate to ammonia and estimation of this by the standard methods. A correction is made for any ammonia already in the sample Reduction with Devarda's alloy is an effective technique[9,17].

2.3.22 *Nitrogen: Nitrite*

For some time, the accepted method[9] was that of Griess Ilosway with sulphanilic acid, which is diazotized in the presence of nitrite and is coupled with 1 : naphthylamine to give a red coloration. The latter reagent, however, is carcinogenic, and other methods have been devised to replace it. One is that of Crosby[18], who employed Cleve's acid (1-naphthylamine-7-sulphonic acid). A less sensitive alternative is the formation with meta-phenylene diamine of a brown colour (Bismarck Brown).

2.3.23 *Total Salts*

These are usually determined by the conductivity measured under controlled conditions, the instrument used giving readings that indicate, or can be related to, the content of dissolved salts in the water[8]. If an instrument is not available, a known sample volume can be evaporated to dryness and brought to constant weight to give total solids by evaporation. The residue ignited at 500–600°C is cooled and weighed to give total inorganic matter[9].

2.3.24 *Anionic Detergents and Non-ionic Detergents*

The method for the determination of anionic and non-ionic detergents is given below in Section 13.2.13 of Part II.

2.3.25 *Fluorescent Brightening Agents (FBA)*

There is as yet no standard method for the determination of these substances. A qualitative examination can be made by the evaporation of a specimen down to a small bulk and immersion in this residue at the boil of a small swatch of cotton, nylon, and polyester-fibre yarns. The FBA will dye onto the fibre to which it is substantive. The comparison can be made semi-quantitative by selecting an FBA of the type found and making comparison dyeings under known conditions with which the specimen dyeing can be compared.

2.3.26 *Oil, Grease, and Fat*

These substances would be in small amounts in any but polluted waters, and analytical methods would have to be suited to the objective if it were desired to distinguish between them. The total extractable matter is probably best determined by direct treatment with a low-boiling solvent, such as methylene chloride, preferably in a continuous-extraction apparatus. The solution in the solvent is then distilled under vacuum to remove the volatile material and the residue weighed.

3. SOURCES OF WATER: COLLECTION, CONTROL, AND DISTRIBUTION

3.1 Surface, Bore-hole, and Mains Supplies

The main sources of water are watercourses (rivers, streams, and canals), bore-holes, and mains supplies.

Many textile works have supplies of surface water taken directly from a river or impounded in reservoirs. This can vary greatly in quality from place to place and also, in rivers, with time. Small streams tend to give more uniform supplies than rivers because they are less likely to be contaminated, and storage in reservoirs tends to provide uniformity. Canal supplies vary greatly: some are uniform, whereas others change abruptly because of contamination.

Bore-hole water, particularly from deep supplies, is usually very uniform, but the composition depends almost entirely on the geological source. Shallow wells generally contain much water that has reached them from the surface, and this may bring varying amounts of contamination.

Mains supplies may come originally from both surface and bore-hole sources, but, where the water undertaking is dealing with large quantities, they are generally fairly uniform. The fact that a water is potable does not, however, necessarily make it suitable for textile purposes. Organic matter is found in many mains supplies from moorland sources, and this, although small in amount, can give deposits in pipes and storage tanks that can cause soiling when disturbed. Some waters contain fine silt, which, although innocuous to humans, is filtered out by textiles and gives rise to staining. Both these types of contaminant must be removed by flocculation and filtration.

Mains supplies of potable water have been regarded generally as of reasonably high standard, apart from the suspended matter in some and the hardness of others. However, the reorganization of water resources may lead to the use of lower-quality water or, as is worse from the textile finishers' point of view, water that may vary from time to time. This makes difficult the maintenance of a uniform high quality within the textile works and may necessitate careful watch on the raw water to anticipate the effect of changes in composition. Whereas the user of surface water had once to cope only with changes due to weather (i.e., silt in storm water), of which some warning was obtained, in future the change may occur without warning in mains water.

3.2   Storage

Textile works that use surface or bore-hole water generally have several lodges or reservoirs to give a uniform stock for use. The capacity of these may be several days' supply, and, with a more or less continuous inflow, the level changes little, and there is a substantial amount of clarification while standing. There is often, in addition, a 'ready-use' reservoir or tank that can be kept under observation, with the feed controlled by the water man to suit the usage. At this stage, waters from two or more sources are sometimes mixed, so that the outflowing water is of fairly constant composition.

Trouble is often experienced with the growth of algae in storage reservoirs and tanks; this occurs when the retention time in the reservoir is two days or more. The only certain method of prevention is to exclude light from the water, and the employment of a light aluminium roof on a tank is becoming common practice. If it is not possible to do this, various additions can be made to kill the growth, but, unless dosing is maintained over the growing period (usually May, June, and July in the U.K.), the algae can return. Substances used are chlorine, potassium permanganate, sodium arsenite, copper salts, and algacides, such as Panacide (BDH) and Algistat (BDH). An effective dosage has been found to be 1 mg/1. of chlorine, applied as sodium hypochlorite. The quantity needed may, however, vary according to the quantity of organic matter in the raw water.

After purification treatment, the process water can be stored in elevated tanks and fed by gravity to the machine, or it can be pumped directly with only a small balancing tank overhead. The gravity feed is more expensive in that large overhead tanks are needed, whereas the pumped supply can give water at high pressure but is dependent upon trouble-free running of the pumps. The gravity feed has another advantage in providing an adequate supply for fire-fighting when the works is shut down.

3.3   Construction Materials: Tanks and Pipework

Construction materials vary considerably and are determined to some extent by the water quality. Tanks for hard water can be of cast iron or sheet steel, but for soft water the sheet metal has to be protected by bituminous or plastics coatings. For pure-water storage, particularly if hot (as is water from heat exchangers), plastics with glass-fibre reinforcement or plastics-lined steel can be used. Piping and fittings should also be non-corrodable, and suitable materials are cement–asbestos, rubber-lined metal, or plastics (poly(vinyl chloride)). Cold purified water can be transferred in polythene or pitch-fibre pipes, but these should not be used in locations where hot water can be accidentally passed through the pipes. The transfer of near-boiling water through bitumen-coated pipes can have disastrous results.

4. WATER TREATMENT

4.1 Sedimentation and Filtration

Sedimentation and filtration for the removal of solid matter from process water are essential for most textile uses, and the methods employed depend mainly upon the source of the water.

Many textile works use surface water from streams or rivers, and, to obtain a uniform supply with a substantial reserve, this is often collected in reservoirs or lodges. The slow movement in these storage basins allows some of the suspended matter to settle out, and the clarified water is taken for use. It is a natural development to use further reservoirs or special settling tanks to carry on the process of clarification, to remove substantially all the solids in suspension. Where there is some coloration of the water or fine silt settling very slowly, the water can be dosed at this stage with an agent such as aluminium sulphate, to produce a flocculant precipitate that settles fairly rapidly and carries down colour and silt. If this is done before passing through a settling tank, the sludge produced can be removed continuously or at fixed intervals, so that the clarification is not interrupted for tank-cleaning.

The amounts of flocculating agent have to be determined by trial on the water itself, some waters requiring more than others. Insufficient agent will give poor clarification, whereas too much is wasteful and may sometimes give poor results. It is important to maintain the pH of the water near to the neutral point because the rate of flocculation and the efficiency of clarification fall off on either side of neutrality. (The dosage of aluminium sulphate is usually within the range 10–100 mg/l.) If, after the addition of the agent used, the pH is outside the limits 6–8, then correction should be made by the addition of small amounts of alkali or acid at the same time as the flocculant. Laboratory trials should always be made to ascertain the most effective dosing conditions for the water that is to be treated.

The use of 'activated silica' as an addition to the alum coagulant gives speedier flocculation and a more stable floc, so that it is employed fairly extensively. The activated silica is prepared by the addition to a solution containing 1·5–1·8% sodium silicate of an acid to bring the pH down to 5.

This solution is then diluted further for use. The amount employed (as SiO_2) is usually between 10 and 40% of the quantity of aluminium sulphate used, but the best ratio has to be found by trial. A period with slow stirring to allow time for the floc to form is an important stage in the flocculation treatment.

Settling tanks can be of several types, and they use the principle of slowing the rate of flow of the water to allow the solid particles to fall out as a sludge that can be removed separately. Using this principle in its simplest form are rectangular and circular tanks, comparatively shallow in depth. In these, the water flow is from end to end or from middle to side, respectively, the clear water leaving by weirs or troughs, and the sludge on the bottom being removed by mechanical scraping gear that carries it to a sump from which it can be pumped away. The upward flow tank, usually conical or pyramidal in shape, with its widest part at the top, allows the water to flow up with diminishing speed, the solid matter falling to the base, from which it can be removed as a sludge by the hydrostatic head in the tank, scraping gear being unnecessary. A development of this has an inverted cone as a centre section, the water flowing down with heavy solids dropping to the bottom and then upwards at a controlled speed, so that falling lighter solids are balanced in the flow to form a 'sludge blanket', which acts as a buoyant filter catching very fine particles. Sludge can be removed from the bottom and also withdrawn from the sludge-blanket zone. The clarification of water by means of sedimentation becomes more complex with the use of dosing methods and upward-flow tanks, but, with analytical checks on the treatment, the results can be much more consistent than with the simpler settlement in mill lodges, and there need be no interruption in supply caused by variations in the raw water or the need for cleaning out tanks.

Bore-hole water rarely contains a large quantity of suspended solids, but, if it contains iron or manganese in solution, the removal of these entails the production of a precipitate that has to be removed by methods similar to those given above.

Filtration of water is generally done through a bed of sand of fineness around 0·5 mm (retained on a 30-mesh sieve), suitable for taking out the suspended matter without becoming rapidly blocked with solids. The old type of gravity filter is rarely found nowadays, and most works use pressure filters containing beds of graded sand, coarse at the bottom and fine at the top, through which the water is pumped from top to bottom. When the pressure difference between top and bottom reaches 5–8 lbf/in^2 (34·5–51·2 kPa) it shows that the bed is becoming clogged and requires cleansing. The flow is then reversed by a system of valves and the bed backwashed. This releases the solids, which go to waste, and leaves the bed clean for reuse. This backwashing is usually preceded by raking or aerating the sand bed to disturb the sludge and free the sand; this assists the backwash water in removing compacted sludge. With several sand filters, one can be undergoing backwashing while others are in use, and this permits continuous filtration of the supply. With only one or two filters, it may be necessary to have adequate storage for filtered water to keep up the supply while filters are out of action. Often it is necessary to have some storage of clean water for backwashing, and this is conveniently done by having an elevated tank for the storage of filtered water, the head of water giving sufficient pressure for backwashing.

Flow rates in pressure filters are usually around 3 gal/min per ft^2 (154·4 l./min per m^2) of filter surface area, whereas backwashing has to be at a high rate, usually 10 gal/min per ft^2 (514·5 l./min per m^2) of bed area, for 5–10 min. A sight glass on the backwash vent line gives visible indication of the progress of washing.

New developments in filtration have been mainly in the direction of improving performance and lengthening the times between backwashing. One method has been the use of graded materials that reverse the normal sequence and give coarse material at the top and fine at the bottom. This gives filtration in depth, the larger particles being taken out near the surface and the finer ones lower down resulting in greater filtration capacity. The bed is made of a fine dense material and coarse light material, so that, after disturbance in backwashing, the former settles first and the latter afterwards, the bed thus being re-formed in the correct order.

Another method reverses the direction of flow, with the water moving upwards through coarse and then fine material. Cleansing of the medium is achieved by an increase in flow, which suspends the particles in the water dislodging the less dense sludge.

A hybrid of sedimentation and filtration is the recent method in which a sand slurry moves down a tower, and water is passed from the centre to the perimeter across the sand stream. The sand carries away suspended solids and is air-lifted to the top, where the turbulence frees the solids from the sand as sludge. In a separation section, the sludge is discharged, the clean sand going back into the system, so that the process of filtration is continuous and the 'filter' is self-cleaning.

Filtration of water is often combined with flocculation, the chemicals being fed into the supply at some point before the filters and the sand removing the floc and suspended solids together. This can be conveniently arranged by means of a dosing pump connected to the main pump drive so that the dosage is proportional to the flow. The quantities of chemicals are adjusted in the same way as was described with reference to sedimentation.

4.2   Softening

4.2.1   *Cold Lime–Soda-softening*

This process, which is of some antiquity, depends on the very low solubilities of calcium carbonate and magnesium hydroxide. When hydrated lime is added to water containing calcium and magnesium bicarbonates, calcium carbonate is given by the former and magnesium hydroxide and calcium carbonate by the latter. These are all precipitated to leave very small quantities (15–17 p.p.m.) in solution. The addition of lime has to be matched to the known hardness of the water and to the distribution of this between the calcium and magnesium hardness.

Thus:

$$Ca(HCO_3)_2 + Ca(OH)_2 \longrightarrow 2CaCO_3 \downarrow + 2H_2O,$$

and:

$$Mg(HCO_3)_2 + 2Ca(OH)_2 \longrightarrow 2CaCO_3 \downarrow + Mg(OH)_2 + 2H_2O.$$

Twice as much lime is required to remove the magnesium hardness as that needed for the equivalent of calcium. Magnesium salts of stronger acids, such as the sulphate, chloride, or nitrite, normally grouped under permanent hardness, are removed in the same way to give a precipitate of the hydroxide, i.e.:

$$MgSO_4 + Ca(OH)_2 \longrightarrow Mg(OH)_2 \downarrow + CaSO_4.$$

Calcium salts produced in this way, and also those occurring naturally, can be removed by treatment with sodium carbonate, e.g.:

$$CaSO_4 + Na_2CO_3 \longrightarrow CaCO_3 \downarrow + Na_2SO_4.$$

The costs of the process depend directly upon the temporary and permanent hardness of the water and upon the relative amounts of calcium and magnesium compounds that are present. As mentioned above, to remove magnesium bicarbonate hardness requires twice as much lime as is needed for calcium bicarbonate. Calcium permanent hardness requires the more expensive sodium carbonate, whereas magnesium permanent hardness requires both lime and sodium carbonate.

The addition of the necessary chemicals can be made at the same time, and the plant requires means for adding these, mixing them with the water to give time for interaction, and removing the precipitate by sedimentation, usually by some variation of the 'upward-flow' type of tank. This gives continuous rapid clarification of the softened water.

Iron and manganese bicarbonates can be removed in the cold lime–soda treatment by pre-aeration, followed by precipitation as the insoluble hydroxides.

A considerable amount of sludge comes from lime–soda-softening, the amount increasing with the hardness of the water. The solid matter consists of calcium carbonate and magnesium hydroxide, together with iron or manganese hydroxide and any suspended matter that was in the raw water. The disposal can present a problem for a large works, and space has to be allocated for allowing the wet sludge to drain and for storage before the solid can be carted away. It is an innocuous material, so that it does not cause a nuisance, but the quantity can be embarrassing. It could be a useful raw material if there were locally a need for mild alkali in this form.

4.2.2   *Zeolite-softening*

Treatment of water utilizing the principle of ion-exchange, whereby the calcium and magnesium ions in water were interchanged with sodium from a solid medium, started with the use of natural zeolites, complex hydrated silicates. Methods of manufacturing such zeolites were found later, and these were made with a capacity for the interchange of cations greater than that of the natural materials. The interest from the water-treatment aspect is that the cation-exchange can be reversed. After use for the removal of calcium and magnesium ions from water, the material can be regenerated by treatment with excess of sodium chloride solution to restore the sodium zeolite complex, and the zeolite may be used in a series of softening–regenerating cycles. The bed is never allowed to become exhausted, since this would permit incomplete softening and be wasteful of salt; it is regenerated just before the stage at which hardness in the outflow becomes perceptible. This enables softening to be done simply and economically with waters of a wide range of hardness by passing them through a bed of the granulated material. Up to a limiting range of flow, the water can be almost completely softened without any difficulty in control.

With very hard waters, the softening effect is incomplete, but the residual hardness is not more than 1–2 % of the initial figure.

Softeners are usually large steel pressure vessels with supports for the zeolite filling and an arrangement of piping and valves so that either water or salt solution can be circulated through the bed. For regeneration, a known volume of salt solution or a given weight of salt is used at fixed intervals of time or volume of water. For intermittent use, tests on the treated water can be made to show when regeneration is needed.

Automatic installations are becoming more common, and these have advantages in conserving manpower and avoiding erratic regeneration. They are generally operated on a fixed cycle, so that, when a known volume of water has passed through the plant, a valve is turned so as first to backwash the bed to cleanse the zeolite, and then to pass in brine for a fixed time to regenerate the material. Water is next passed in to remove residues of salt and regeneration products, and finally normal running is restored.

Automatic systems depend upon the hardness of the water being substantially constant, and if there is any variability they are too inflexible. In such cases, a partly automatic system is better, in which the time for regeneration is set by the operator after tests to determine the water hardness.

In addition to calcium and magnesium ions, the zeolites remove small quantities of iron and manganese, but it is inadvisable to allow appreciable quantities of these ions into the system, since they are not removed in regeneration.

The capacity of the zeolite for softening depends upon its source and the conditions of regeneration. In theory, 1·2 lb (0·54 kg) of common salt is required per pound of hardness (as $CaCO_3$) but in practice about three times this amount or more is employed. Calculations based on those of Nordell[19] give the relationship shown in Table III.

Table III
Effect of Salt Consumption on Water-softening Capacity

Water-softening Capacity		Salt Consumption		Ratio: Salt/Capacity
(lb/ft³)	(kg/m³)	(lb/ft³)	(kg/m³)	
1·14	18·3	3.2	51·3	2·8
1·28	20·5	4·0	64·1	3·1
1·43	22·9	5·0	80·1	3·5
1·71	27·4	8·0	128·1	4·7

This table shows the increase in capacity obtained with greater salt consumption, and economical running generally has to be a compromise between these two factors.

In backwashing and regenerating the base-exchange medium, a fairly concentrated solution containing sodium and calcium chlorides is produced. This is normally run off with other effluents without difficulty, but care may be needed if the waste water contains soap, because insoluble lime soap may precipitate in the drains and cause blockages.

4.2.3   *Other Methods of Softening Water*

It is possible to soften water by the addition of chemicals that displace or combine with the calcium and magnesium, such as sodium hexametaphosphate and ethylene diamine tetra-acetic acid. They remove the hardness, and the former gives sodium salts instead of the calcium and magnesium salts. Even lime soaps can be dispersed and solubilized, so that there is the basis of a useful emergency treatment that can be applied when the normal supply of soft water is not available or where, for some reason, hard water has been run into a vessel and it is desired to counteract its effect *in situ*.

Another use for the sequestering agents is to immobilize metals that might cause difficulties in processing. For example, copper and iron can cause instability in peroxide bleaching baths and damage to cotton during bleaching. The addition of ethylene diamine tetra-acetic acid or diethylene triamine penta-acetic acid to the bleach bath reduces the deleterious effects of the metals.

4.3   Iron and Manganese Removal

Ferrous and manganese bicarbonates are slightly soluble and can be present in some types of ground water. On exposure to the air, ferric and manganic hydroxides are formed as flocculent solids. These can be deposited on textiles as the hydroxides or can combine with fatty acids to give metal soaps, which cause staining that is difficult to remove. When known to be present, iron and manganese can be easily removed from water, and there are several processes that are used for this purpose.

The commonest method is simple aeration of the water, which oxidizes the ferrous or manganese salt and gives a precipitate of ferric or manganic hydroxide. This can be done in slatted or packed towers or, if required, under pressure, by the injection of air.

In some of the normal methods of softening, iron and manganese are removed. Provided that air is excluded, base-exchange methods can be employed. Clear deep well waters can be treated in this way, but. if any air is allowed to enter, the precipitated hydroxides will clog the treatment bed and obstruct the passage of the water.

In lime–soda-softening, small amounts of the metals are removed from solution with the calcium and magnesium, and, with prior aeration, large amounts can be dealt with by this process.

Manganese bicarbonate, although similar in its reactions to ferrous bicarbonate, is more soluble. It is usually, but not always, associated with iron in natural waters. Even very small quantities can be troublesome and cause brown staining when the hydroxide is deposited. For removal by aeration, the alkalinity must be raised to above pH 9·5.

In addition to the bicarbonate, iron is sometimes found in water as ferric hydroxide, which can be removed by filtration, and as ferrous sulphate, which requires aeration, neutralization, and settling or filtration. Iron combined with organic matter cannot be removed by the methods applicable to iron in the ionized form, and it is usually necessary to remove it by flocculation with alum or alum with sodium aluminate, followed by filtration; the final pH should be adjusted so as to be close to neutrality on the alkaline side.

In continuous processes, a filter medium containing manganese dioxide oxidizes the iron and removes it as the ferric hydroxide. The material is generated by backwashing and treatment with permanganate.

4.4   Acidity and Alkalinity

These should be considered together with pH, for the latter is the indication of the departure from neutrality.

Acid water may come from moorland sources or from streams containing mine drainage or effluents from other works.

Alkaline waters may come from hard-water sources or from the softening processes. Zeolite-softened water may be quite alkaline because it contains substantial quantities of sodium carbonate and bicarbonate.

Usually, pH limits of between 7 and 9 are desirable, that is, no acidity and only bicarbonate alkalinity, although for some purposes stricter limits may be necessary. For example, at elevated temperatures, sodium bicarbonate decomposes and releases carbon dioxide and leaves sodium carbonate as mentioned earlier[5]. The alkalinity is increased, and this may disturb some textile processes.

5.   WATER RESOURCES ACT, 1963

This act controlled the abstraction of water from watercourses, springs, wells, and bore-holes, so that any user of appreciable amounts was required to be licensed to take water for industrial and other purposes. Existing users could apply for 'licences of right', which permitted them to take quantities up to the maximum that had been abstracted previously. A charge was made for the abstraction, and this was based upon the maximum figure on the licence. The control under the Act covered all users of water, apart from those taking town supplies, whether they were pumping from a river or had installed extensive catchment works at their own expense.

New users of water or those who require more than the maximum amount scheduled in an existing licence have to apply for permission to take the estimated quantity to the water authority in the area in which the works is situated, which will then decide whether sufficient water is available for the new abstraction. If the water is available, a licence is issued, which gives the conditions under which the water can be taken, but, if there is insufficient water, the authority can refuse a licence or issue one for a smaller quantity. It is therefore essential for a new user of water to make a licence application as early as possible. This applies both to surface- and ground-water (bore-hole) supplies, but not, of course, to town water.

6. COSTS

A survey made in 1964 showed a wide variation in charges for water made by local authorities and water boards[20]. The range was from less than 5p per 1000 gal (4546 litres) to more than 15p per 1000 gal, often with a sliding scale, so that large users were charged at lower rates. There seemed to be little relation between charge and geographical location, except in Scotland and Northern Ireland, where the cost of water was low.

Costs for water obtained from local natural supplies were difficult to obtain, and few figures were available. Most firms regarded the cost as low and confined mainly to power used for pumping and to maintenance.

Softening costs can be appreciable and depend upon the method employed. Base-exchange treatment is in the neighbourhood of 1·5–4p per 1000 gal (4546 litres), automatic systems tending to be lower than manually operated plants. Lime–soda treatment costs vary with the water composition.

PART II: THE TREATMENT AND DISPOSAL OF EFFLUENTS

7. INTRODUCTION

The disposal of trade effluents has become an important factor in running factories in many industries all over the world, and attention has to be given to methods of dealing with waste waters in order to select the most economical methods, both in running costs and in capital expenditure. Furthermore, the textile industry is an easy target for the conservationist because an effluent coloured with waste dye attracts attention, however small and innocuous the amount of colour may be.

The quantities of waste water are often great, so that a treatment plant designed to cope adequately with them may have to be large and therefore expensive to install. Some methods of treatment require plants that cost more than others, whereas some processes may have much lower running costs. The selection of the method of purification of the wastes therefore has considerable influence on the plant costs.

In addition, textile effluents are very variable in flow and composition, so that the treatment process has to be able to cope with all the fluctuations that can occur from day to day or month to month. The character of the waste from a dyehouse or printworks could alter considerably with changes in the textile processing arising from variations in the materials handled. This makes it important for the designer of the effluent plant to have knowledge of the textile methods and for him to be informed of changes that may occur.

The wastes that go down the drain come from two main sources, the textiles themselves and the residues of chemicals employed in treating them. A great deal of the organic matter in the waste comes from the fibres, this being sometimes more than half the total amount in the effluent, particularly with some of the natural fibres. This is not often realized by people outside the industry, who have adversely criticized the discharge of contaminating liquors on the assumption that wasteful methods have been employed. In fact, the more economical methods may have led to stronger liquors being discharged because the water has been the vehicle by which unwanted impurities have been removed from the textiles and put down the drain.

The other source of contamination, the chemicals, may offer some hope of economy in use, but here many are employed to produce particular effects and are discarded after use. Again, economy in water usage may give rise to higher concentrations in the wastes for the same usage of chemicals. This does not mean that considerable economies have not been, or cannot be, made. Careful attention to processes and the disposal of spent baths can often have beneficial effects, while changes in methods can produce very large changes in the character of the effluent. Thus a peroxide-bleaching process produces a less obnoxious effluent than a kier-boil–hypochlorite bleach, and change to the peroxide method might be advantageous provided that the resulting textile product and the costs were acceptable. Any marked change in processing has to be considered with care because the effect on the effluent-treatment process might be disastrous.

On the other hand, changes can often be made in the textile process which can have a beneficial effect on the effluent, either by reducing the volume or strength or by making it more treatable.

The diversity of the components of a textile effluent is very great, probably only matched or exceeded by that of the tanning industry, which is well known for its variability.

8. PRINCIPLES OF EFFLUENT DISPOSAL IN THE UNITED KINGDOM

A firm producing trade effluent in the course of its work has to dispose of it in a manner that does not interfere with production and does not contravene the limitations laid down in the relevant Acts of Parliament. There are usually only two possible methods of disposal: to the local-authority sewers for treatment or to a watercourse. For either method, conditions are imposed on the volumes, rates of flow, and composition, and these are normally contained in a 'consent', setting out in detail what is required. Where discharge is to a sewer, the conditions will be mainly concerned with items that might affect the operation of the sewage works, whereas effluent going to a stream would have to be purified to a high degree, and limits deal mainly with residual substances that could cause pollution or toxicity in the river water.

There has been in 1974–75 reorganization of the water-controlling bodies, and at about the same time there has been new legislation on pollution. The new water authorities took over not only river management but also potable water supplies and sewage treatment, a somewhat cumbersome organization. The individual authorities are divided into departments dealing with each of the main fields, and in practice it is with these that the industrialist will have contact. The Control of Pollution Act, 1974, covering solid-waste disposal, air pollution, and noise in addition to water pollution, is an inconveniently complex document, which the trader will find difficult to interpret in terms of action needed to meet its demands. The Act endows water authorities with wide powers to enforce those sections dealing with trade effluents and waste disposal. Parts of the older acts have been repealed, and the main effects are to give stricter and wider control of effluents, the ability to stop discharges, and, in the case of rivers, the power to charge for disposal. Up to the time of this Act, the controls were on volumes and peak flows, temperature, alkalinity or acidity, potential pollution levels (as measured by Biochemical Oxygen Demand and the content of suspended matter), and the maximum levels of several known toxic substances. Under the new Act, the latter items are brought under an all-embracing 'poisonous, noxious, or polluting matter', which is not defined further, although in another section mention is made of pollution 'injurious to the fauna or flora of a stream', which is very difficult to interpret or demonstrate in the light of the complexities of work in this field. Furthermore, the textile finisher wants to know which of his materials are *not* injurious, which is even more awkward to define, because many things may be innocuous at one concentration but toxic at another, or not poisonous in one system but injurious in another owing to the presence of pollutants from another source.

It is understood that consents under the new Act will contain extensive lists of prohibited or restricted materials, and the discharges will have to be kept within the limits on each under threat of severe penalties. This may work for simple effluents, where the composition is known in detail, but for textile wastes such is rarely the case. The matter in a textile effluent comes from two sources, the textiles that the finisher handles in the course of his work, and the hundreds of chemicals that he employs in his processes. Over the former he has little or no control, because the impurities are present on the textile fibres when he receives them, and the added sizes and softeners are put on by the spinner or weaver and may come from outside his firm, or indeed from other parts of the world. One part of the finisher's job is to remove such non-fibrous substances in the purification processes, and whatever is removed goes down the drain.

The chemicals employed in the textile processing may be known, but some by-products are formed, and there are many complex auxiliaries used of which the detailed composition is unknown. It would be economically, if not practically, impossible to ascertain *all* the components of the waste water. For example, of the hundreds of proprietary products in use, many are mixtures of which the composition is known only to the suppliers, who may be outside the country. The dyer also uses upwards of several hundred dyes, chosen according to need and properties from many thousands available. It would take facilities beyond even those of the water authorities to keep track of the composition and amounts of these.

One section of the Act states that registers containing details of effluents must be kept by the authorities and open to public inspection. Such disclosure of use could be against the interests of finishers. In certain cases, a certificate of exemption could be obtained, but the risk would always be present.

Taking a broad view of the Act, one can readily see that the textile firm will find it more difficult to meet imposed conditions, and it will be more expensive to dispose of effluents. The industrialist in his daily work has to be concerned with chemicals and materials in production, and now he has the added burden of finding out how they affect the trade waste. Not until information percolates back will he know that he has broken the regulations, and then the difficulty arises of tracing this to a particular substance or combination of conditions. This will be extremely difficult to do, especially when it has taken place several weeks before, and yet it will have to be done to prevent a recurrence. It would appear that a great deal of effort will have to be spent by both the textile industry and the water authorities to achieve a practical solution of these problems.

The choice between discharge to a watercourse and that to a sewer may be difficult. In the former, the waste liquors usually require purification, and the capital and running costs of a treatment plant may be high. For sewer disposal, the cost of treatment by the local authority has to be ascertained as well as the cost of any pre-treatment, such as neutralization, that may be required. The charges made by local authorities are based on their own treatment costs for sewage, and the unit costs of these may be higher in small communities.

Comparison of the estimated costs of treatment by the firm's own plant and by the local authority will show the cheaper method, but other aspects have to be considered. If a firm runs its own treatment plant, the responsibility for the final discharge is its own, and the water authority can take action against it for infringement of the discharge conditions; charges can now be made for discharge to a stream. On the other hand, if the firm discharges to a sewer, this responsibility is thrown on the local authority. The charges by the local authority for treatment may and probably will increase in time, and this can be serious if new treatment plant is brought into service by the local authority and high loan charges are included in the basic costs. Recent large increases in treatment costs in several textile areas show this trend.

Methods of charging for treatment are not uniform throughout the country, and the imposition of a charge is not obligatory. The arrangement with the industrialist can be by agreement or by 'consent'. If the former, it can be wide-ranging, and the method of calculation and the conditions are laid down in a document agreed between the two parties. Unless means of varying the terms are included, those set down stay in force while the agreement is operative. Open-ended agreements whereby no means of termination are provided will not be permitted in future. Such an arrangement does not give the industrialist the protection under the relevant Acts of Parliament, and, if a dispute arose, it would have to be settled in a court of law. There may, however, be advantages under an agreement, such as favourable terms for the payment of charges or easier restrictions that could not be maintained under other methods.

By a consent, the authority may impose limitations on flow, temperature, or composition and can make charges for handling, treatment, and sludge disposal. Charging methods vary, but one in common use indicates the type of calculation employed. The payment is based upon total volume, and the charge is in three parts, i.e.:

$$\text{charge per 1000 gal (4546 litres)} = A + B.\frac{O_T}{O_S} + C.\frac{S_T}{S_S},$$

where A includes pumping, preliminary treatment (if applicable), and general expenditure;

B covers biological treatment;

C covers solids treatment and sludge disposal;

O_T and O_S are the BOD values (see below) for the trade waste and sewage, respectively; and

S_T and S_S are the SS (suspended-solids) values for the trade waste and sewage.

The unit costs, A, B, and C, are calculated as average values from the sewage running costs of the works and the proportions of depreciation and loan charges for the appropriate parts of the works.

Until recently, the unit costs tended to be much lower for a large works than for a small one, but, with the reorganization of the water services and the much heavier overheads, this may no longer hold. The conditions of a consent can be changed at intervals of not less than two years. The great advantage of a consent is that, if the discharger is aggrieved at the conditions imposed (but not at the fact that he may be charged for effluent treatment), he can appeal against the conditions to the Department of the Environment provided that the appeal is made within the stipulated period from the imposition of the consent or the revision of the consent. The case is then put to an inspector of the Department, who will decide whether the appeal is reasonable and, if so, what charges should be made.

Another factor that has to be considered is the method of analysis for estimating the effluent strength on which the charges are based. The Biochemical Oxygen Demand (BOD)* has often been employed for this and, where treatment is on a biological plant, is probably the fairest means of estimating the load on a plant. Owing to the length of time, five days, that elapses before results are obtained, some sewage works have used other tests. The Permanganate Value (PV)† was the first of these, and for domestic

---

* See Section 13.2.5.   † See Section 13.2.6.

sewage there is a rough correlation between the PV and the BOD, so it was employed for day-to-day control of the biological treatment. However, for industrial effluents and for textile wastes, the results do not bear much relation to BOD values. For example, liquors containing readily oxidizable chemicals (such as sodium sulphide in sulphur-dye liquors) show a very high PV for a given BOD, the oxidation being taken far beyond that which would take place in the aerated or biological treatment, or the permanganate could oxidize substances that might be unaffected by the aeration process. In consequence, charges based on the PV could be much higher than those based on the BOD, to the detriment of the industrial discharger.

An appeal against the use of PV (and its derived quantity, the McGowan Strength) was upheld by the Department of the Environment in the case of a dyeworks effluent that contained residues from vat- and sulphur-dyeing.

More recently, the Dichromate Value (DV)* has been employed in certain areas, and this deviates still further from the BOD. This is because the DV, like the PV, is a measure of substances that may include not only those contributing to the BOD but also others that may not be biologically degradable and are therefore not included in the BOD. The results of DV tests on textile wastes are almost always higher than the BOD figures but not uniformly so. The DV may be several times the BOD, but the actual ratio between the two will depend on the composition of the effluent at the time of sampling. Charges based on the DV may be from two to three times the amounts paid previously. This fact, with increases in running costs and loan charges by the authority, may put textile works at a serious disadvantage in the regions using the DV.

9.   TYPES OF TEXTILE-WORKS EFFLUENT

9.1   Introduction

The processes used in textile works need no introduction to textile finishers, but the properties of the liquors discharged may not be so familiar from the point of view of effluent treatment. It is worth while surveying the processes that are responsible for the bulk of the pollution in wastes and to consider some of their properties that affect the treatment processes used. A paper on the treatment of textile waste liquors deals with this in some detail[21].

9.2   Scouring

The liquors from cotton-processing, particularly those from desizing and kier-boiling, contain much organic matter, mainly derived from the natural impurities of the cotton and from sizing materials in fabrics. Although the organic matter can be removed by biochemical means, the high concen-

---

* See Section 13.2.7.

trations present have to be brought down by dilution in a uniform manner, since otherwise the treatment plant may be overloaded at times when desizing baths or kiers are being run off.

Treatment of synthetic fibres or blends does not produce so concentrated a liquor as that from cotton, but the amount of organic matter from size and anti-static agents in the cloth may still be appreciable.

Scouring liquors for raw wool are well known for their high content of emulsified wool grease and other substances derived from the wool, which give highly polluting liquors. Scouring liquors for wool yarn or fabric contain much less grease, but they may have much of the olein or synthetic oil that has been applied to the yarn in processing, together with soap or detergents.

9.3 Bleaching

Bleach liquors contain the residues of oxidizing agents, such as sodium hypochlorite, sodium chlorite, and hydrogen peroxide, as well as alkalis or acids. Residual peroxide is not detrimental, but the other oxidizing agents may have to be reduced or kept out of the treatment plant, and excess acid or alkali always has to be neutralized.

9.4 Mercerization

Mercerizing wastes usually contain considerable amounts of caustic soda, and this has to be neutralized. It can be collected separately and some recovered or reused in the works. The weaker wash liquors may not be worth collecting, but they have to be neutralized. It is usually more convenient to do this at source rather than allow the liquor to mix with the main flow of waste and treat it after dilution.

9.5 Dyeing

Dye liquors vary greatly in composition, but the components common to most are dye residues and the dyeing assistants, usually agents with surface-active properties. In addition, certain dye liquors contain substances that can be troublesome in purification treatments. Sulphur-dye liquors contain sodium sulphide, which has to be removed or diluted before treatment. Chrome-dye liquors and some after-treatment solutions contain metals that can interfere seriously in biochemical processes, and these have to be segregated or rendered innocuous.

9.6 Printing

Printing wastes contain the thickeners employed in the paste and substantial amounts of dye pigments. From the effluent point of view, there are three sources of these:

      (i) colour pastes surplus to requirements;

      (ii) residual colour on machines, screens, and rollers; and

      (iii) loose colour on fabrics.

A great deal can be done to minimize (i) by precise forecasting of amounts needed and attention to detail in the making up of the pastes. The residual colour from cleaning after a printing run can be collected and treated separately, particularly when water conservation in this section avoids the use of large volumes of water. Preliminary sedimentation, with or without a flocculating agent, will eliminate a good part of the colloidal and solid matter.

9.7 Finishing

Finishing is such a wide field that it is difficult to pick out individual substances that have to be considered in the effluent treatment. The residues of various starch fillings are probably those to be found in the greatest quantity. Most of these come from surplus materials in mixing and machine boxes. Other finishes, being more expensive, are employed less wastefully, so that little unused material is discarded.

9.8 Weaving

Weaving gives rise to size residues, of which most of the material in the effluent comes from washing out becks and sow boxes. Weaving on water-jet looms now produces appreciable amounts of waste water.

10. FACTORY DRAINAGE

In most established works, the drains from machines are embedded in the floor, and in most works little can be done about it except to ensure that the whole system is known, so that the source and path of waste liquors can be established and the records kept up to date.

If individual machine drains are accessible, it is possible to segregate particular flows for separate treatment, and this can be useful in wastes that can cause trouble or that need special treatment. This applies to drains from sulphur-dye baths, kiers, mercerizing machines, and wool-scouring ranges.

The materials commonly employed for drains are stoneware (vitrified clay) and cast iron, but in some new plants plastics drainpipes are being employed because of their resistance to corrosive chemicals[22]. Polythene and poly(vinyl chloride) have been employed in this way, and glass-fibre-reinforced resin pipes are useful in special circumstances. The insertion of a plastics lining in an existing defective stoneware or iron drain may save an expensive repair bill. Pitch-fibre pipes are useful, too, in dealing with corrosive liquors below the boiling point of water. For the segregation of wastes, it is sometimes possible to lay a plastics pipe inside a larger-diameter drain, advantage being taken of the flexibility and chemical resistance of the plastics material.

11. PRELIMINARY TREATMENT

In most textile wastes, it is important and even essential to mix and balance the waste liquors to even out large variations in composition, temperature, and flow. It is convenient to neutralize excess alkali or acid at this stage, so that the balanced liquid is in a condition to go forward for further treatment. Some removal of gross solids, such as rags and lint, can also be achieved by the use of a screen, preferably one of the self-cleaning kind.

The mixing to even up the composition has to be done by deliberate mechanical or hydraulic means, and it is not sufficient to let the flow pass into a tank and hope that it will mix itself. A storage tank to hold the greater part of the day's flow is desirable, and some elimination of peaks in concentration can be obtained by fitting baffles that force the liquid to move from top to bottom and back again. It is more effective, however, to install slow paddles that mix the levels of liquid in the tank, and the same result can be obtained, usually at lower power consumption, by the use of a hydraulic 'gun' that takes the water from the bottom and discharges it at the surface in a semi-continuous flow[23].

The work of blending can be eased by segregating concentrated liquors and letting them discharge slowly over a long time and by recovering heat from hot process liquors, so that these solutions do not fall to the bottom or float on the surface. If the heat is not recovered, it may be necessary to cool the waste water in order to conform to temperature limits. This can be done by passing through ventilated cooling towers, where evaporation of some of the water effects cooling of the bulk. Other methods include passing the water through shallow lagoons or spraying it into the air, where radiation and evaporation produce a drop in temperature.

Neutralization usually involves the treatment of liquids containing either mineral acid or alkali. Acid removal is often needed in the wool section of the textile industry and can be accomplished by the addition of lime or caustic soda. Lime, being cheap, is employed for large treatment plants, and caustic soda, although dearer, is usually simpler to use for smaller plants.

High alkalinity is commonly brought down by dosing with sulphuric acid, usually ROV grade. The addition of alkali or acid usually requires some form of dosing mechanism worked by a pH meter–controller, so that the inflow of liquid with a pH outside the neutral zone causes the controller to open a dosing valve and add acid or alkali, as required, until the pH is brought back within the required limits. Quick dispersion of the added acid or alkali is needed, and, with large fluctuations of flow and concentration, it has been found that one dosing stage is insufficient. Two or more dosing systems in cascade allow the control of a wide range of concentrations. These systems are arranged so that, if the first system adds insufficient material, the next system operates, and so on, until the neutralization is completed (Fig. 1). If this method is not adopted, it is found that either the applied dose is insufficient or marked 'hunting' occurs, with the pH over-shooting and returning at frequent intervals.

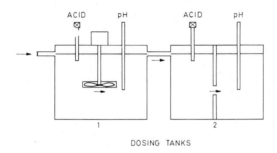

DOSING TANKS

Fig. 1
Diagram of an acid-dosing system

Some firms are removing caustic alkalinity by carbonation, the source of the carbon dioxide being flue gas from the works boilers, which usually contains 10–12% CO_2 in normal running. Carbonation with flue gas can be done in a packed absorption tower, with the alkaline liquor sprayed or per-colating down, while the flue gas is blown or drawn up the shaft. Excess of gas is used, and, by control of this and the liquor flow, the alkalinity can usually be brought down to the neighbourhood of pH 9. The caustic alkali is con-verted substantially to bicarbonate; further reduction of pH is more difficult and is usually unnecessary. Local authorities will generally accept a top pH limit of between 9 and 10, and, for treatment in the firm's own plant, a limit of 10 is adequate. With the correct flow settings, the pH control is automatic as the system comes into equilibrium with the excess of flue gas. Because little corrosion occurs in the presence of the alkaline liquors, the plant can be constructed of mild steel, except for those parts in contact with the dry flue gas. It must, however, never be allowed to run dry; suitable safeguards to prevent this can be installed (Fig. 2)[24].

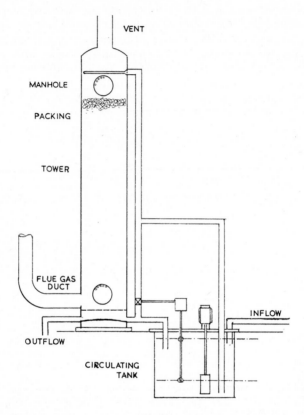

Fig. 2
Diagram of a flue-gas tower for the neutralization of alkaline wastes

As an alternative to neutralization of the main flow of effluent, it is sometimes possible to deal with a few large amounts of alkali or acid at source, and this can be very useful in maintaining control. Examples of this are the neutralization of kier liquors by the addition of a fixed amount of acid on discharge and the continuous dosing of mercerizing wash liquors. A special case of this is the treatment of wool-scouring liquors, where, in order to recover the wool grease, the neutralization is often done batchwise, and the fatty acids and wool grease that are released are separated and collected.

The separation of wool grease from wool-scouring liquors entails breakdown of the grease emulsion, often by the addition of acid to 'crack' the soaps that are present. Liquors from raw wool are often first centrifuged to recover a large part of the grease in a relatively pure state. This grease commands a higher price than that recovered by acid cracking, which contains free fatty acids from the soaps and other impurities.

The method in which acid is used is fairly simple and is widely employed[25]. The greasy liquor is passed through a flock catcher to remove loose fibre and settled or centrifuged to take out any solid particles. Acid is added with mixing to neutralize alkalis and soaps and the acid liquor separated from the sludge (magma) by decantation. The magma can be heated and the liquor passed through a horizontal plate press, or it can be drained, mixed with sawdust, bagged, and pressed in heated vertical presses.

If grease and oil are not recovered, the scouring liquor can be cracked by the addition of calcium chloride, which gives a precipitate of lime soaps and grease or oil, and this can be removed by vacuum filtration to leave the partly purified liquor for disposal[26].

Many textile wastes are low in nitrogenous substances, and for biochemical treatment it is necessary to add nitrogen, usually as ammonium sulphate, in sufficient quantity for the growth of the organisms. It is convenient to do this in the preliminary treatment.

12. METHODS OF TREATMENT

12.1 Flocculation and Coagulation

For the removal from wastes of some of the soluble organic matter and light suspended solids, it is possible to add a chemical agent that forms a blanket of flocculent matter adsorbing some of the soluble material and carrying down solid particles.

Alum and both ferrous and ferric iron salts have been used for this purpose for some time, and their action has been studied in some detail[27,28]. The flocculation conditions should be related to the method of separation of solid from the liquid, since the requirements may differ. Where sedimentation under gravity is employed, the coagulation should be carried out under conditions close to neutrality, say, between pH 6 and 7. Tests should, however, be made with the actual effluent, because components of this may affect the result, and a lower or higher pH range could be more appropriate. Separation by filtration may demand different conditions of coagulation because the requirements here are those of a permeable cake of solid particles on the filter medium, that is, ease of transport of water under pressure (or vacuum) through a fairly thick bed of the flocculated solids. The addition of the flocculating agent has to be made rapidly, so that it is well dispersed before precipitation takes place, and this is followed by slow stirring over a longer period, to allow the flocs to grow in size without being broken down by turbulence in the water. In practice, this demands dispersion of the coagulant in a small well-stirred tank, followed by slow movement in a much larger tank, in which the flocs can form and grow over a longer period of time. This may be easier to achieve under batch conditions than it would be under continuous flow, but local circumstances may dictate the most effective method. The objective is to produce large, stable flocs, which enmesh solid particles so that these can be filtered off or removed by sedimentation. The large floc particles settle rapidly and occlude the finely divided solids that may be in the waste, and clarification in settling tanks is accelerated. Furthermore, the large surface area of the flocculent mass gives an opportunity for the removal of soluble matter by adsorption, so there is also purification by this means. In some cases, as in the use of iron salts in solutions containing sulphides, there is removal of contamination by chemical means, as insoluble iron sulphides. This removal of soluble organic matter by absorption could be very useful where there may be high concentrations or possibly toxic materials present that might interfere with a subsequent biological process. A flocculation pre-treatment could alleviate such difficulties and allow a smaller biological plant to be used.

The amount of flocculating agent required depends upon both the material being added and the composition of the waste. Alum, ferric sulphate, and ferrous sulphate, the common additives employed, are used in quantities of up to, say, 500 mg/l. of aluminium or iron. It is desirable to make trials of the addition at a range of concentrations and to observe that at which clarification is most effective. Too little gives incomplete removal of solids, and too much, apart from being wasteful, may give poorer results and slower settling than intermediate quantities. If concentration of the coagulated solids is to be obtained by means other than sedimentation, then it is important to make further tests by appropriate methods, for example, laboratory trials for pressure or vacuum filtration.

Several organic flocculating agents have been manufactured for specific purposes, these usually being soluble polymeric substances, which, when diluted and added to waste liquors, produce flocs that can be effective in clarification. The quantity of material is usually very much less than that needed for inorganic flocculants, and this to a large extent may offset the higher cost of these organic materials. Some of these materials make effective additives to the inorganic coagulants.

A disadvantage of the inorganic flocculating agents is that the amount of sludge produced is usually greater than that from the suspended solids in the liquor being treated, and allowance has to be made for this in sludge disposal. On the other hand, the large amount of inorganic matter may make filtration more attractive than sedimentation for removing solid matter, continuous processes, such as vacuum or pressure filtration, being used.

12.2 Oxidation by Biochemical Methods

12.2.1 *Introduction*

Soluble organic matter can be removed from waste liquors by biological methods, micro-organisms being used to break down the soluble matter into simpler substances. The soluble organic matter is absorbed on the biological matter and taken into the cell substance, where enzyme and other actions break down the structure, with the production of simpler materials, some of which are used in the cell metabolism. Some stages involve oxidation of the absorbed matter, and this provides energy for growth and reproduction of the cells. Since the process is essentially one of oxidation, oxygen must be provided, this being done by one of a variety of methods employing aeration. This oxygen has to be in solution for the organisms to breathe and to use in their assimilation of the organic matter. The methods have been developed in sewage-works practice, and the main ones are the 'activated-sludge' process and the 'percolating-filter' process. Both of these are continuous processes, the liquor for treatment flowing in at one end of the system and passing out at the other end. The former uses oxidation in aerated tanks, with the organisms floating in the liquid in flocculent masses. The latter uses oxidation in a film of liquid flowing over a solid support to which the organisms can attach themselves. With a permeable medium, air can diffuse through the mass to replenish the oxygen in the liquid that is used up by the organisms. Other conditions have to be suitable for growth of the organisms, such as the pH being not far from neutrality and sufficient nitrogen and phosphorus compounds being present in solution to provide the right balance of these with the carbonaceous matter for assimilation by the micro-organisms.

In more detail, the methods are as follows.

12.2.2 *Aerobic Treatment by Activated-sludge Processes*

12.2.2.1   *Introduction* In these, the micro-organisms are dispersed in the water, the main variants being in the methods employed for aeration[29,30].

12.2.2.2   *Diffused Aeration* Compressed air is fed to porous diffusers to produce a multitude of fine bubbles floating to the surface and presenting a large area for the diffusion of oxygen into the water. The plant arrangement is shown in Fig. 3.

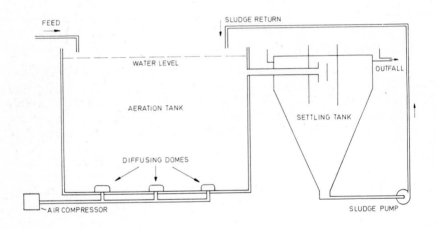

Fig. 3
Diagram of an activated-sludge plant

12.2.2.3   *Mechanical Aerators* Several of these have been developed, and they fall broadly into two classes, those rotating on a vertical spindle and those rotating on a horizontal spindle. Several vertical rotors are available, and these depend upon a beating action of radial blades at or near the liquor surface, combined with the centrifugal action, which throws liquid out over the top layers to mix and entrain bubbles of air (Fig. 4). Horizontal aerators are of the paddle or 'brush' type, i.e., a partly immersed cylinder with radial

blades that beat the surface, churn air into the water, and also circulate the liquid in the containing vessel.

Fig. 4
Biological-treatment plant: activated sludge
(By courtesy of Ames Crosta Ltd)

12.2.2.4 *Coarse-bubble Aeration* A hybrid of the diffused-air and mechanical methods, used abroad but not, as far as is known, in Great Britain, is coarse-bubble aeration, with the bubbles broken up and dispersed by a rapidly rotating propeller. Air at low pressure is passed into the liquid through perforated pipes, which give masses of fairly large bubbles. The surface area for a given volume of air is less than that for the diffused-air method, but the air at low pressure can be obtained from fans, which are cheaper than compressors and require less maintenance.

A variation of this is the 'hydraulic gun', which produces a series of large bubbles in a vertical siphon moving water from the bottom to the top of a tank and aerating by the great turbulence produced as the bubble bursts.

12.2.2.5 *General* In all types of activated-sludge processes, the outflowing liquid contains much solid biological matter, which has to be separated and most of which has to be returned to the aeration system to maintain
the concentration of solids needed for efficient working (see the discussion of
secondary sedimentation and flotation below).

The principal running cost for aeration is in the power required, and this
may be lower for mechanical aeration than for diffused air. Historically,
diffused aeration came first, and a considerable amount is known about it.
Once a system has been installed, it is, however, rather inflexible and can
meet only a limited range of conditions. The mechanical aerator came later
and in a variety of forms has been used extensively. Recently, in the form of
floating aerators, it has been used on tanks, lagoons, and lakes, where the
installation of any fixed system would have been difficult or impossible. The
diffused-air system has nevertheless been employed in packaged plants,
where it lends itself to a standard design of plant that can be fabricated
complete with aeration and sedimentation sections in one unit. For small
units, particularly, this may give an advantage in price because much expensive civil-engineering work can be avoided.

Apart from the methods of aeration of the mixed liquor in the activated-
sludge system, there are now variations in the times of treatment, in the points
of entry of the feed and returned sludge, and in the treatment of the surplus
sludge. These give rise to processes that have acquired their own names
because of the way they differ from the conventional methods.

In the conventional method, the feed enters an aerated zone with a
retention time of say 6–8 hr and then passes to sedimentation tanks in which
the solids are separated and the sludge returned to the aeration tank, surplus
being discarded.

In the 'extended-aeration' method, the aeration time is lengthened about
fourfold to give more complete treatment before settling the solids and
returning the sludge. This requires larger aeration tanks but gives better
control of the treatment.

The 'oxidation ditch' is a variation of the extended-aeration method.
The normal form is a shallow racecourse-shaped lagoon with a central
division. Rotating 'brush' aerators move the liquor bodily round the ditch
while at the same time giving adequate aeration.

The 'contact-stabilization' method feeds the liquor into a sludge that
has been well aerated in a separate tank. The soluble impurities are absorbed
on the sludge with purification of the liquor. After a short time, this goes to
the sedimentation tank, and the effluent is discharged. The sludge and
absorbed organic matter are aerated in another tank for 6–8 hr and then
returned to the initial contact zone. Surplus sludge goes to another tank in
which it is aerated for 20 days.

12.2.3 *Aerobic Treatment on Percolating Filters*

Percolating filters (filter is a misnomer) of the conventional type usually consist of circular or rectangular beds, 5–6 ft thick, of broken stone or a slag medium of uniform size. The medium is supported on channel tiles that allow liquid to drain away while permitting air to have access to the mass. This is shown diagrammatically in Fig. 5. The liquid for treatment is distributed across the upper surface by rotating or traversing sprays according to the shape of the bed and trickles down through the medium to wet the surface on which the biological film grows. Organic matter from the liquid is absorbed by the organisms and is oxidized to simple substances or becomes part of the biological mass. The emergent liquid is substantially free from degradable organic matter but contains suspended matter, which is mainly surplus biological growth that has to be removed by sedimentation or some other method of clarification.

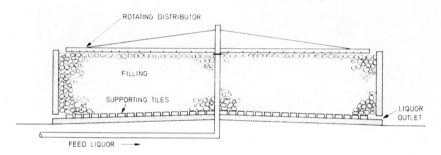

ROTATING DISTRIBUTOR

FILLING

SUPPORTING TILES

LIQUOR OUTLET

FEED LIQUOR

Fig. 5
Diagram of a percolating filter

Many existing filters are composed of 1–3-in. stone or blast-furnace slag, which is somewhat porous. The medium must be unaffected by the liquids under treatment and must not break down under pressure or through temperature changes over a long period.

An important development in percolating filters has been the use of plastics sheet or tube in cellular form[31], which supports the growth of micro-organisms but allows free access of the liquid to be treated and of air, the former at higher rates of flow than are feasible with stone filters. Such plastics systems with high through-put rates do not give such complete removal of organic matter as the conventional slag filters but provide much greater removal in terms of weight per unit volume. They are therefore suitable for roughing treatments and take out a great weight of degradable matter in a compact plant. Plastics units, with their low weight, allow high units to be used so that space is saved (Fig. 6).

Fig. 6
High-rate biological-treatment plant
(By courtesy of I.C.I. Ltd and Teesside Textiles Ltd)

On a dyehouse waste, the removal of organic matter, as measured by the BOD, ranged from 57 to 69 % at flow rates of 40–60 gal/yd³ per hr (240–360 l./m³ per hr), the loadings being up to 1·7 lb/yd³ per day (1·0 kg/m³ per day). The outflow after treatment in an activated-sludge unit or on a conventional percolating filter gave a final discharge within the normal 'Royal Commission' limits.

The high-rate filter could also be employed for treatment of the 'kier liquor' from the scouring of cotton fabric, but it was found necessary to dilute it with dyehouse waste as well as to add nutrient in the form of ammonium sulphate. When undiluted, there was considerable BOD removal, but deposition of matter occurred near the top of the column, which interfered with the biological oxidation. This deposited matter was soluble in organic solvents and consisted mainly of cotton wax and fats. On reversion to a dyehouse waste with no kier liquor, or only a minor quantity of it, the deposit was gradually removed. The proportion of kier liquor that can be handled without causing this difficulty is probably between 20 and 40% of the total flow.

12.2.4 *Anaerobic Digestion*

A method of treatment by biological methods that does not involve aeration is the digestion of warm liquors out of contact with the air. Under these conditions, the organic matter is broken down into simpler substances by certain types of micro-organisms that do not require gaseous oxygen, the final products being carbon dioxide and methane. The reactions do not go to completion, however, and 50–70% conversion is usually obtained. This type of process may be useful for preliminary treatment of sludges and of strong wastes such as kier liquors, where even partial removal will substantially reduce the load that needs to be removed in an aerobic-treatment plant.

In laboratory and pilot-plant trials on the anaerobic treatment of kier liquor mixed with digesting sludge, there was good removal of organic matter and gas production: nutrient salt addition appeared to be unnecessary. The rate of BOD removal increased linearly with the rate of loading up to 24 lb/1000 ft^3 (36 kg/m^3) of digester space. This might be an attractive method where sufficient closed storage space is available because running costs would be low for the removal of a large part of the organic load. Stirring of the digesting liquor is important to keep the contents uniform, and the maximum rate of reaction usually occurs around 35°C. The need for heating could offer difficulties with some wastes, but, for kier liquors and similar hot wastes, advantage could be taken of the retained heat.

Another type of anaerobic treatment is that utilized in digestion ponds in the United States, where liquors are held for fairly long periods, i.e., 90–180 days, while cold digestion proceeds. This, on wool-scouring effluents, was said to be effective, with a BOD reduction of 80–90%. One advantage of this method was the removal of 99% of Dieldrin in the waste, although residues of 0·12–0·37 mg/l. were still regarded as high.

12.3 Sedimentation

12.3.1 *Preliminary Sedimentation*

Preliminary settlement to remove suspended matter is not often necessary before a biological process employing aeration because the solids in textile wastes (apart from wool-scouring wastes and kier liquors) are usually more or less inert, and sedimentation does not reduce the organic load very much. Primary sedimentation for the removal of particulate solids from the wastes may be carried out before anaerobic processing or after chemical treatment, such as flocculation, mentioned previously.

Fig. 7
Radial settling tank

The plant employed is usually in the form of rectangular or circular (Fig. 7) tanks, where the flow, from end to end or middle to side, respectively, allows time for the settlable solids to fall to the bottom and to be removed as a sludge. Some existing tanks are desludged manually, but sludge-scraping gear is becoming common, and this reduces labour costs: the process can also be made automatic. For textile wastes, the vertical-flow tanks, in which the sludge collects as a floating blanket or in a conical base, have not been found satisfactory because they are sensitive to temperature changes, and these can cause density currents that surge through the sludge and carry solids to the outlet. Temperature changes as small as 2 degC can create difficulties of this type[23]. A diagram of a radial settling tank is shown in Fig. 8.

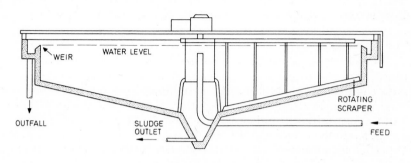

Fig. 8
Diagram of radial settling tank

Tank design should follow good civil-engineering practice, with full-width inlet and outlet weirs on rectangular tanks. Radial tanks should have diffusing baffles on the inlet to prevent the formation of currents by the flowing liquid on entry and to disperse liquids of different densities. Outlet weirs should be of adequate size, and the use of an annular suspended weir or of several radial weirs would be an improvement on a single-perimeter weir. Notched weirs made of non-corrosive metal or impregnated wood offer advantages in ease of setting and in durability.

A fairly recent trend has been the fabrication of steel settling tanks, which are as effective as, but less expensive than, concrete or brick tanks.

12.3.2 *Secondary Sedimentation*

Secondary sedimentation, following biological treatment, involves removal of the biological solids that have been formed and, in the activated-sludge process, rapid return of the sludge to the aeration system. The normal practice is to use either circular radial-flow tanks with scraper gear or upward-flow tanks. The temperature variations of the crude waste have been ironed out by the time the aeration stage is complete, and upward-flow tanks can be employed when the process is continuous. If flow is stopped at a week-end, they should not be used. Where sludge has to be returned to the plant, the settling tanks have to be as small as is practicable, so that solids are not held for times that allow them to become septic through complete consumption of the oxygen in solution. In calculations of flow rates, however, it is important to allow for the increased flow due to the volume of returned sludge.

Where sludge is not being discarded, this may be a substantial increase on the normal feed rate to the plant. The return of sludge at a controlled pumped rate is better practice than intermittent manual control or the splitting of flows between the returned sludge and the surplus sludge.

12.3.3 *Flotation*

Instead of the separation of particulate solid matter as a sludge by sedimentation, it is possible to cause the suspended particles to float to the surface of the water and collect them as a thicker layer, much as cream upon milk. This can be achieved by compression of air in contact with part of the water, which causes it to dissolve. As soon as the pressure is released on injection into the main mass of fluid, the dissolved air is released as a cloud of fine bubbles, which become attached to any solids and cause them to rise to the surface. The mass of solids, water, and air is continuously skimmed off and gives a sludge that contains a greater quantity of solid matter than that produced by sedimentation. Flotation is also much quicker than settlement, and, for an activated-sludge plant, the solids can be returned to the aeration system more rapidly and in better condition.

Another method employs the electrolytic generation of gases *in situ*, which, in the form of gas bubbles, rise through the liquor from grids in the base of the vessel and carry up floating particles in the same manner as that of compressed air.

12.3.4 *Sludge Disposal*

The soluble organic impurities in wastes are converted in the biological processes to solids that are finally rejected as a sludge containing between 1 and 3 % insoluble matter. Since this is comparable in weight with the original weight of organic soluble substances in the effluent, there is a considerable amount of sludge for disposal, and this presents a difficult problem in a large works. Some waste-disposal firms will take away sludge in tankers; some local authorities will accept sludge in their own disposal plant, but these solutions only remove the problem to second-hand. For treatment, a common method is to run the sludge into drying beds with porous bases, usually cinders or sand, in which the bulk of the water is removed by a combination of drainage and evaporation. Drainage of the sludge is, however, slow, and drying to a level of water content that allows the solid cake to be lifted may take many months, particularly in wet weather. This means that the area of drying beds has to be large to cope with the output through the year.

It is helpful as a preliminary treatment for the sludge to be put through a thickening tank, in which the solids sink and can be drawn off as more concentrated slurry, while the supernatant liquor can be decanted off. The more concentrated sludge requires less space on drying beds and less equipment in other methods of disposal.

Some sludges can be dewatered by vacuum or pressure filtration, but this is dependent upon the properties of the sludge under pressure. Where the solid particles in the sludge deform under pressure, the solid mass that is first filtered out can become more or less impermeable to water and slows down the rate of filtration so much that the process is impracticable. The sludge properties are affected by their conditions of formation, by the methods of handling, and by subsequent chemical treatment. For example, the rate of loading in an activated-sludge-treatment plant will affect the sludge properties, some conditions giving sludges that filter with difficulty. High rates of shear in pumping will change a sludge so that filtration becomes difficult. Treatment with flocculating agents, either inorganic or organic polyelectrolytes, can improve the filtration behaviour. The subject is very complex, and detailed knowledge of the effluent being treated, the conditions of processing, the filtering properties of the sludge, and its response to chemical after-treatment are all needed to deal adequately with the problem of sludge disposal.

Concentrated sludges and filter cakes can be brought down to their inorganic constituents by incineration in multiple-hearth furnaces or in fluid-bed incinerators, but these methods are only practicable for large works.

12.4   Additional Treatment for High Purification

12.4.1   *Introduction*

The biochemical treatments mentioned can be expected to remove 90–95% of the soluble organic matter in the waste, expressed as BOD. For a liquor originally containing, say, 400 mg/l. BOD, the final waste will have a BOD of between 40 and 20 mg/l. This may not be low enough for some requirements, but it would be uneconomical to increase the plant size to remove the remainder, apart from the fact that the residual matter may be more resistant to biological treatment than the part that has already been removed. Several methods have been shown to give additional purification, and these are described below[32]. A good deal of the residual BOD comes from the fine suspended matter in the discharge, and, if this can be removed, there is a substantial improvement in the effluent.

12.4.2   *Grass Plots*

If the liquor is allowed to flow over a plot of coarse grass on a slight slope and collected at the bottom end, it is found that there is an appreciable reduction in both BOD and suspended solids. Alternatively, the liquor can be applied to the plot by methods similar to those employed for spray irrigation. The area required is about 1 acre (0·4 ha) for each 150,000–250,000 gal/day (682–1137 kl/day) of liquor to be treated, so that, for firms with space available, this gives a simple method of polishing the effluent. The grass and low-growing plants play an important part in trapping solid particles and increasing the available wetted area of the plot. It is convenient to have several similar plots, so that one can be in use and the others resting or being renovated.

12.4.3 *Slow Sand Filters*

The slow sand filter, of the type commonly employed for water treatment, consists of a bed of graded sand, fine at the top and coarse below, through which water flows by gravity. It removes suspended solids but can also, by the biochemical action of organisms held between the grains, mainly in the upper layers, remove some of the residual soluble organic matter in the effluent. This gives a marked polishing effect and requires little attention after installation except for backwashing and re-forming the bed when too large a quantity of filtered solids interferes with the flow.

Through-put rates can be expected to be in the region of 1 gal/hr per ft^2 (49 l./hr per m^2) of filter-bed surface, so that the method is mainly suitable for small flows.

12.4.4 *Micro-straining*

A third method, called *micro-straining*, involves the use of a moving mesh filter arranged on the circumference of a drum-shaped support rotating on a horizontal axis, through which the liquor flows under a low head. The solid particles taken out are washed off in a separate zone, and the cleaned mesh filter is returned to use, all in a suitable cycle of operations. The removal of the suspended particles gives a reduction in both the BOD and suspended solids. The capital cost of micro-strainers is greater than that of the other two methods mentioned, but the through-put rate is high: 90–150 gal/hr per ft^2 (4405–7342 l./hr per m^2) of total filter area for coarse mesh and 40–80 gal/hr per ft^2 (1980–3960 l./hr per m^2) for fine mesh, so that the method allows further treatment where space is limited.

12.4.5 *Lagoons*

Lagoons have been used for treatment in various ways for some time, although the function of the lagoon has not always been appreciated. A large shallow sheet of water purifies wastes by a combination of settlement and biological action. Fine solids have time to settle out if the rate of flow is slow, and soluble matter is removed by organisms, including the algae, which thrive in sunlight. The results obtained can vary considerably owing to the fluctuations in suspended solids carried away, but generally lagoons are less effective than the use of a similar area as grass plots (Section 12.4.2 above). In use, the main difficulty arises in cleaning out the deposited sludge, which, if allowed to accumulate, could decompose anaerobically and, because of gaseous fermentation, could cause masses of sludge to rise to the surface in warm weather.

12.4.6   *Removal of Residual Soluble Matter*

The removal of residual soluble matter, as distinct from suspended material, is difficult but fortunately is only required when the removal of specific substances is required, such as residual dyes or proofing chemicals. The quantities involved may be very small, but the effect may be marked; a minute amount of dye may colour a whole stream. In such cases, adsorption of the offending material may be undertaken after the normal treatment has removed the bulk of other contaminants. Active carbon is generally employed for this purpose because its adsorbent surface is very great for a given weight of solid. Other substances are adsorbed at the same time, and it is important to select a grade of carbon and the right conditions to give the maximum removal of the dye. The treatment can be effected by the addition of powdered carbon and later removal of the carbon with its adsorbed chemicals, or the liquid can be passed through columns of granular material in sequence. In the former method, the carbon is often discarded after use, whereas in the latter the granular medium is regenerated by controlled combustion and the carbon used again. The choice depends upon the scale of working and the economics of regeneration.

13.   ANALYTICAL METHODS

13.1   Sampling

Sampling prior to analysis of textile wastes presents serious difficulties because of the great variations that occur in flow and composition. A sample should be truly representative of the whole of the waste water that has passed in a given time. Even if the flow were constant and the composition variable, there would be a need to collect a great number of specimens and mix them into a composite to obtain a reasonable sample. When the rate of flow also varies, this method cannot be easily adopted, although attempts have been made by mixing the specimens in volumes proportional to the flow at the time each was taken. Another method sometimes employed has been to take specimens at fixed intervals of volume-passing and to mix equal quantities of these. Neither method is satisfactory because, between the times when specimens are taken, the composition may change greatly, and nothing is available to show what has occurred meanwhile. The problem has been solved by the employment of the method of continuous abstraction of a small volume that was a fixed small fraction of the total flow at the time. When the flow doubled, the sampling rate doubled, and, when the flow fell to half, the sampling rate was halved, and so on. Collecting the small flow in a vessel gave, at the end of the collection time, a composite that was truly representative of all that had passed in the main flow during this time. The instrument originated at the Shirley Institute and is now being developed and made commercially[33]. A study of sampling methods has been published by the present author[34].

13.2 Analysis

13.2.1 *Introduction*

After sampling, the analysis is carried out, and tests of value in assessing effluent quality are listed below (most of these are given in detail in the main book on the analysis of wastes[9] and its predecessor[35]).

13.2.2 *Acidity and Alkalinity*

The measurement of pH by suitable indicators shows the reaction of the waste, and, for those away from neutrality, the titration of acid or alkali gives a quantitative measure of the amount present. The alkali is usually titrated to phenolphthalein and to methyl orange indicators, to obtain the amounts of caustic and carbonate alkali present. By convention, this is often expressed in mg/l. of calcium carbonate to align with the usage of water analysis, but, for the works chemist, it is more convenient to use milli-equivalents, so that it is easy to convert to corresponding weights of acid for neutralization.

For coloured or turbid liquors, the use of a meter with a glass electrode for pH measurement is essential. This is also used for the continuous recording of pH in treatment plants.

13.2.3 *Suspended Solids*

This quantity is determined by the filtration of a known volume through glass-fibre paper, drying and weighing the residue, and expressing the result in mg/l. of solids[36].

13.2.4 *Dissolved Oxygen*

In the Winkler test for dissolved oxygen, manganous hydroxide is precipitated and combines with the oxygen dissolved in the water to form higher hydroxides. These, on acidification in the presence of iodide, liberate iodine quantitatively and can be determined by titration with thiosulphate.

Sample collection has to be done by methods that avoid the loss or gain of oxygen by exposure to the air or change in temperature, and the specimens have to be kept in completely full stoppered glass bottles.

The amount of oxygen in solution varies with temperature, atmospheric pressure, and salinity and can change owing to consumption by reducing agents and oxidizable organic matter in the presence of micro-organisms.

There are various modifications that avoid interference by substances such as nitrite that might be present in solution and could consume oxygen. If any of these are suspected of being present, the appropriate methods given in the book mentioned previously[9] should be used.

There are available various dissolved-oxygen electrodes that permit rapid estimation of the amount present in solution. These usually depend upon the penetration of oxygen through a thin plastics membrane into a bimetallic cell, the voltage of which depends upon the oxygen content of the solution. The best known is the Mackareth electrode[37], which uses a thin polythene membrane round a cell of which the outer part is silver and the inner part lead, with a nylon separator. The free space in the cell is filled with sodium bicarbonate, which avoids any air bubbles. By the use of a thermistor temperature corrector, the cell can give a voltage reading that is a direct indication of percentage saturation with oxygen. Calibration is by means of two solutions, one deoxygenated by the use of a reducing agent and the other saturated with air at a known temperature. These give the zero and 100% saturation points on the instrument scale, and intermediate figures are obtained on the assumption of a linear response.

13.2.5   *Biochemical Oxygen Demand (BOD)*

A considerable amount has been written on this test[9], which was evolved originally as a measure of the consumption of dissolved oxygen by river water. Water at 20°C contains about 9 mg/l. of dissolved oxygen, the concentration varying a little with atmospheric pressure. When water contains organic matter, micro-organisms can utilize this for growth by consuming some of the oxygen. For given conditions of time and temperature, the oxygen consumption is a measure of the organic matter that is capable of being assimilated by the organisms. Where organic matter is present in quantity sufficient to use up most of the dissolved oxygen, the conditions in natural waters change, and a state of pollution exists. The BOD has therefore become a measure of the polluting tendency of wastes, but it can also be employed in treatment plants to indicate the organic load on the plant.

The details of the test have to be followed meticulously, since only in this way can reproducible results be obtained. On the basis of the Winkler method for dissolved oxygen, measurement is made of the amount in solution before and after a standard incubation. The liquor to be tested is diluted to a suitable level and a known volume added to oxygen-saturated water containing trace elements and an inoculum of organisms. Closed bottles are incubated at precisely 20°C for five days, and the residual dissolved oxygen is compared with that on duplicates measured before incubation. The difference gives the consumption of oxygen due solely to the organic matter present. Trials have to be made with different dilutions of the test solution, both to observe the effect of dilution and to arrive at a level whereby about half the dissolved oxygen present is consumed in the test.

The source of the dilution water may affect the results of the test because traces of organic matter can consume oxygen, while residues of chlorine in tap water can interfere seriously with the biological action. Blank determinations are normally made to measure such effects. It is also important to have the diluted samples close to and slightly above the incubation temperature, so that an increase in temperature does not cause a loss of oxygen. This can introduce an error, particularly in blank determinations. The writer has found dilution with deionized water to be preferable to the use of distilled water, since the latter may contain traces of volatile organic matter.

13.2.6 *Permanganate Value (Four-hour)*

In this test[9], the consumption of potassium permanganate under acid conditions by a known quantity of waste liquor is measured after keeping the liquor for 4 hr at 27°C. This test has been employed extensively in measurements of the capacity of sewage to consume oxygen where there is a moderately constant relation between this test and the BOD, and it can be employed to give a quick indication of the expected BOD. For textile liquors, there is little relationship between the permanganate-value (PV) results and those of BOD measurements, and the ratio of the two can vary over a wide range; the value of the test is therefore limited.

13.2.7 *Dichromate Value*

This analysis measures the consumption of acid dichromate at the boil for 2 hr under reflux. The original method has been largely superseded by the small-scale method[9,38], which is just as accurate but more convenient. The figures obtained are generally higher than those for BOD on the same specimens because it includes most of the organic matter, both degradable and undegradable. Although rapid and chemically accurate, the method does not necessarily give figures that bear the same relationship to BOD values on the same samples; in fact, for undegradable materials that would not cause river pollution, high dichromate values (DV) and low BOD values may be obtained. The method does, however, give a reasonable measure of the content of organic matter.

13.2.8   *Nitrogen: Ammoniacal*

This may be present in various forms, but the one likely to be of interest to the effluent chemist is that in solution as ammonia or related compounds[9]. The method of determination of these is by making the solution alkaline with magnesium oxide, distilling the liberated ammonia into a known quantity of sulphuric acid, and titrating the excess acid with sodium hydroxide. In the preparation of solutions, ammonia-free water must be employed and precautions taken to prevent contamination by ammonia or volatile amines from the atmosphere.

13.2.9   *Nitrogen: Organic, Nitrate, or Nitrite*

This has been dealt with in Sections 2.3.20–22.

13.2.10   *Grease*

This is usually determined by solvent extraction, either of grease extracted by a flocculation technique or by direct treatment of the liquid with droplets of a dense low-boiling solvent, such as methylene chloride, but the technique is difficult. In an elegant variation of an earlier method used by the Wool Industries Research Association[39,40], a known quantity of waste is taken up on paper tissue, and this is dried and rapidly extracted with solvent in an apparatus that evaporates the solvent continuously after it passes through the tissue. This allows quick estimation of grease and oil without the difficulties associated with the extraction of liquids by liquids.

13.2.11   *Chlorine*

Residues of bleach liquors may be present in wastes, and large quantities can be estimated by titration in the normal manner with thiosulphate or arsenite[9]. Small quantities of up to 1 mg/l. can be estimated by the red colour obtained with the DPD reagent (*p*-amino-*N*:*N*-diethylaniline sulphate) at pH 6·3, this being compared visually with standards corresponding to known concentrations or measured absorptiometrically.

13.2.12   *Sulphide*

The presence of soluble sulphide in wastes may be determined by the release of hydrogen sulphide on acidification, displacing it by means of a stream of inert gas (carbon dioxide or nitrogen), and collection in zinc acetate solution[9]. To this is added a known quantity of standard iodine solution, and the excess is titrated with thiosulphate.

Another, more rapid, method is potentiometric titration with ammoniacal copper solution, for which platinum–calomel electrodes are used[41]. This method will cope with strong sulphide liquors as well as dilute residues.

13.2.13 *Detergents*

The standard test for small quantities of anionic detergents is that of Longwell and Maniece[9,42] in which methylene blue in alkaline solution forms a complex with a surface-active agent that can be extracted with chloroform. The extract is treated with an acid solution of methylene blue and the optical density compared with that of standards prepared in the same way.

Non-ionic surface-active materials are determined by extraction under standard conditions and estimation by thin-layer chromatography. By using known solutions for comparison, the spot density allows an estimate to be made of the quantity present in terms of the surface-active agent used as a standard[43].

A variation on the test demonstrates the presence of degradation products, which may be a useful feature in studies of the breakdown of detergents in treatment plants.

14. FLOW MEASUREMENT

In work on effluents, it is important to know the volume of liquid flowing, both for the estimation of the total load on a treatment plant and for the interpretation of analytical figures from process liquors. In many places, it is obligatory to install some form of meter for measurement of the discharge to the local-authority sewer or to a river.

Flow measurement in practice comes down to a limited number of methods, all of which have their applications according to local conditions.

(i) Very large flows: by the measurement of the depth of water over a weir, this being translated to flow by accepted formulae.

(ii) Moderate or small flows: by the use of inferential water meters, in which the motion of a propeller or vane is translated into terms of flow, or by electrical methods.

(iii) Both large and small flows: by the direct measurement of the volume flowing into a vessel or tank in a given time.

The first of these methods is generally employed for the estimation of large flows in open channels, where a weir with a gap of known shape produces a difference in level above the gap that is proportional to the flow. The water-level difference can be measured by means of a float or by a pneumatic dip tube.

For a V- or rectangular-shaped notch, the relations are as follows:

$$\text{V (90°) notch:} \quad F = 2{\cdot}6 \, H^{5/2},$$
$$\text{rectangular notch:} \quad F = 3{\cdot}3 \, LH^{3/2},$$

where F = flow,

H = difference in water level, and

L = width of the rectangular notch.

With dimensions in feet, the calculated flow is in ft³/sec; if metres are used, the flow is in m³/sec.

A variation on this method is the use of the venturi flume, which produces a level difference in the water flow that can be measured in a manner similar to that of a rectangular weir, and this can be translated into terms of flow by using the same formulae. An advantage of the venturi flume is that the loss of head produced is less than a weir in the channel in which it is installed, and it does not normally require a stilling tank, such as is used for notched weirs.

Inferential flowmeters, normally used on pipes that are full of liquid, are obtainable already calibrated, so that, by installation in a suitable position, the flow in the pipe can be read directly. It is important to ensure that the mechanism does not become clogged with floating debris, particularly fibrous matter, so that the use of these flowmeters is normally limited to clean-water lines. A fairly long stretch of straight piping upstream of the meter is necessary for reliable results to be obtained. The electrical type of meter has no protruding parts in the water stream and is not affected by suspended matter.

The third method listed is a simple and accurate one that can be employed either for flow estimations in the course of the work or for the calibration of meters. The requirements are a vessel or tank of known volume, a stopwatch, and means for diverting the flow into the measuring vessel. The vessel can be a bucket or drum with litre or gallon marks or, at the other end of the scale, an empty tank or reservoir that can take part or all of the works flow. By measurement of the volume filled in a known time, the average rate of flow can be determined with accuracy. In bleaching and dyeing works, the process vessels may often serve as tanks of known volume, and the number of times these are emptied gives a measure of the effluent flow, provided that running rinses are not employed.

The recording of effluent flows from works is usually done by the first method, the changes in liquor level being estimated at a notch or flume and these being converted at the instrument into flow rates. Many instruments also have an integrating device that sums the flow over unit intervals of time and gives the total volume that has passed the meter.

In any use of a meter, it is important if accurate records are to be obtained to have an instrument that will handle the highest flows that are likely to be experienced in normal running. With a meter that is too small, the reading is cut off at the top limit, and no information is available at the times that have most effect on the total volume that has passed.

15. REUSE OF WATER

As yet, in the textile areas of Great Britain, there is no shortage of water generally, nor will there be for a long time to come, although there may be local limitations arising from undue abstraction of water. There have been large increases in water charges, however, and these will rise still more in the future, so that it may be economical to limit water consumption and to consider how water may be saved by recycling or reuse after purification.

Not a great deal of water is wasted in the finishing section of the textile industry in spite of what has been said by critics outside it, and normal good housekeeping methods will cope with this aspect of water use. There are, however, processes where better-quality water is used than is necessary, and there is scope here for economy. In the many washing processes that are employed, it is possible to take relatively clean wash waters from one process and use them in another, where the small content of chemicals that they have already picked up would be harmless. For example, the rinses after bleaching could be collected and used for rinsing after scouring without detriment to the latter process. By recycling in this way and careful selection of the rinse waters, it is possible to make great savings of up to 40% of the total water usage[44].

Another important method is by contra-flow washing, that is, washing in stages against the movement of the fabric, so that the cleanest water meets the final fabric and moves back until the dirtiest water meets the unwashed textile material. This method is in common use in many washing ranges, and in some, such as those after mercerizing, may result in a strong wash liquor that may justify recovery of the alkali or reuse as alkali in another process. Where the whole effluent is purified before discharge, the question is often asked whether this could be used again as process water. There are obvious advantages that would accrue if this could be done, apart from the saving in water usage, but there are many difficulties. The main ones arise from the materials that are not removed in the normal purification.

Inorganic salts pass through unchanged, and a high salt content may upset dyeing processes. If the content remained constant, allowance might be made for it, but it is likely to fluctuate, and this could give rise to difficulties.

Dye residues would cause shade variations, particularly in bleaching, and, more insidiously, fluorescent brightening agents can upset the dyeing of pastel shades by affecting the light emission. A pale blue might appear as lavender because of this effect.

On the whole, it would be unwise to consider complete reuse after purification unless the water shortage is serious, and even then recycling may afford a remedy that is simpler and more controllable.

16. COSTS OF EFFLUENT TREATMENT

It is very difficult to make a general statement on effluent-treatment costs because so many factors are involved. On the one hand, we have the volume and composition of the discharge and the variability in composition, which must be allowed for. On the other hand, there is the type of treatment required, together with the need for pre-treatment (i.e., neutralization or flocculation), nutrient addition, and sludge treatment and disposal. It is recommended that in a particular case the following procedure should be adopted:

   (i)   measurements should be made of flow spread over a considerable period to bring in any abnormal or seasonal conditions;

  (ii) sampling should be done in a systematic manner and analysis made of BOD, DV, pH (and alkalinity or acidity), N (ammoniacal), and any suspect materials that might interfere with processing;

 (iii) laboratory trials should be made by a method appropriate to the composition (as shown by (ii)), to determine the ameanability of the waste to treatment;

 (iv) if a satisfactory method can be selected, pilot-scale trials should be made by taking waste directly from the main works flow; this will give process data that can be used for full-scale plant design;

  (v) the information obtained can be referred to a consultant or to firms in the effluent-treatment industry and quotations obtained for plants;

 (vi) the proposals should be compared with the basic data for effluent flow and strength and selection made of those plants which can be expected to cope with these effectively; and

(vii) at this stage, it is possible to make some comparison of capital and running costs with the charges that would be made by the local authority for treatment of the waste (provided that it is possible for such treatment to be made at the sewage works; the local works may be too small or too overloaded to cope with it); discussion should also be arranged with the water authority so that its requirements are known and its co-operation obtained if it should be necessary to discharge treated waste to a watercourse.

ACKNOWLEDGEMENTS

The author and publishers wish to thank Messrs Ames Crosta Mills & Co. Ltd (Fig. 4) and Imperial Chemical Industries Ltd, Agricultural Division (Fig. 6), for kindly supplying original photographs and granting permission for them to be used in this monograph.

REFERENCES

1 'Concerning the Bleaching Industry', the Bleachers' Association, Manchester, 1925.
2 'The Use of Water by the Textile Industry', Textile Research Conference, Nottingham, 1973.
3 'Effluent Treatment and Water Conservation', Committee of Directors of Textile Research Associations, 1970.
4 A. H. Little. *J. Soc. Dyers Col.*, 1971, **87**, 137.
5 T. H. Morton. *J. Soc. Dyers Col.*, 1967, **83**, 177.
6 W. Stump. *Amer. Dyest. Rep.*, 1966, **55**, P680.
7 W. S. Holden (Editor). 'Water Treatment and Examination', Churchill, London, 1970.
8 'Approved Methods for the Physical and Chemical Examination of Water', the Institute of Water Engineers, London, 3rd edition, 1960.
9 'Analysis of Raw, Potable, and Waste Waters', H.M.S.O., London, 1972.
10 'Standard Methods for the Examination of Water and Waste Water', American Public Health Association, New York, 12th edition, 1965.
11 British Standards Institution. 'Methods of Testing Water Used in Industry', B.S. 2690: Parts 1–14: 1964–72.
12 A. G. Knight. *Proc. Soc. Wat. Treat. Exam.*, 1960, **9**, 72.
13 D. C. Abbott and J. R. Harris. *Analyst*, 1962, **87**, 387.
14 'Organic Reagents for Metals', Hopkin & Williams, Chadwell Heath, Essex, 1955 and 1964.
15 Reports of Director of Water Examination, 1947–52, Metropolitan Water Board, London, p. 54.
16 A. B. Wheatland and G. F. Lowden. *Chem. & Industr.*, 1955, 1469
17 W. F. Waters. *Proc. Soc. Wat. Treat. Exam.*, 1964, **13**, 298.
18 N. T. Crosby. *Proc. Soc. Wat. Treat. Exam.*, 1967, **16**, 51.
19 E. Nordell. 'Water Treatment for Industrial and Other Uses', Reinhold, New York, 1951, p. 345.
20 Collaborative Report No. 1, Committee of Directors of Textile Research Associations, Nov., 1963.
21 A. H. Little. *J. Soc. Dyers Col.*, 1967, **83**, 268.
22 'Factory Drainage Materials' (Proceedings of Symposium), Society of Chemical Industry, London, 1965.
23 A. H. Little. Shirley Institute Pamphlet No. 92, 1966, p. 77.
24 K. Barnes, J. S. Franklin, and A. H. Little. *Dyer*, 1969, **142**, 427.
25 E. V. Truter. 'Wool Wax', Cleaver-Hume Press, London, 1956.
26 E. Bowes, J. F. Colville, and J. S. Franklin. *Chem. Engng*, 1964, April, 68.

[27] D. G. Miller, M. Robinson, and J. T. West. Water Research Association Technical Paper TP 43.

[28] J. H. Harwood. *Industr. Chem.*, 1953, **29**, 315.

[29] J. R. Simpson. 'Waste Treatment', Pergamon Press, Oxford, 1960, p. 31.

[30] A. B. Wheatland. Shirley Institute Pamphlet No. 92, 1966, p. 35.

[31] 'High Rate Biofiltration using Plastic Filter Media', No. 4, 'Paper and Textiles', I.C.I. Ltd.

[32] 'Notes on Water Pollution, No. 22', Water Pollution Research Laboratory, H.M.S.O., London, 1963.

[33] Cotton Silk and Man-made Fibres Research Association. B.P. 1,255,624–5 (17 Jan., 1968).

[34] A. H. Little. *Wat. Pollut. Control*, 1973, **72**, 606.

[35] Association of British Chemical Manufacturers and Society for Analytical Chemistry. 'Recommended Methods for the Analysis of Trade Effluents', Heffer, Cambridge.

[36] K. V. Melbourne. *J. Inst. Sew. Purif.*, 1964, Part 4, 392.

[37] 'Water Pollution Research', H.M.S.O., London, 1963, p. 130.

[38] R. J. Fearn, W. H. Hetherington, S. M. Jaeckel, and C. D. Ward. *J. Soc. Dyers Col.*, 1967, **83**, 146.

[39] T. Green, R. P. Harker, and F. O. Howitt. *J. Text. Inst.*, 1956, **47**, T110.

[40] R. P. Harker. Private communication.

[41] Private communication.

[42] J. Longwell and W. D. Maniece. *Analyst*, 1955, **80**, 167.

[43] S. J. Patterson, E. C. Hunt, and K. B. E. Tucker. *J. Inst. Sew. Purif.*, 1966, Part 2, 190.

[44] S. S. Gopujkar. *Dyer*, 1970, **144**, 47.

INDEX